A FIELD GUIDE TO

the
NATURAL HISTORY
of the
SAN FRANCISCO
BAY AREA

JOHN C. WILLIAMS
and
HOWARD C. MONROE
Biology Department
College of San Mateo

McCutchan Publishing Corporation
2526 Grove Street
Berkeley, California 94704

Standard Book Number: 8211-1207-4

Library of Congress Catalog Card Number: 77-107672

To Sue Jan Monroe and Gayle Williams

"To a person uninstructed in Natural
History, his country or seaside stroll
is a walk through a gallery filled with
wonderful works of art, nine-tenths of
which have their faces turned to the
wall. "

T.H. Huxley

"Were I to await perfection, my book
would never be finished. "

History of Chinese Writing
Tai T'ung
13th Century

Table of Contents

PREFACE TO THE SECOND EDITION

This book was originally published under the title of "A Natural History of the San Francisco Peninsula". Since its introduction, it has been used extensively throughout the entire San Francisco Bay Area by students, naturalists, and other interested persons. Therefore we are changing the title of this book so that it may be more representative of its actual coverage and applicability.

The idea behind this book is to foster an understanding of the natural history of our surroundings so that we may better understand the potentials and cope with the problems of our environment. There have been many good reference books written about the plants or birds, or geology of this area, but no single book comprehensively covers all facts of interest. While this book is by no means meant to be a thorough chronicle of every plant, animal or geological feature, we hope it will serve as an introduction to many of those aspects of Bay Area life that make this area interesting and unique.

Several unique factors to be discussed later, tend to give this area the mild, pleasant climate that makes an extremely wide range of life forms possible. This unique biological situation may yield interesting horticultural arrangements in back yards of this part of California, but it presents a biological nightmare for any author who attempts a systematic study of this area. We will attempt to bring out and clarify many such interesting relationships. Most of the specific areas discussed in this text are located on the San Francisco Peninsula but similar biomes can be found in most bay area counties.

We wish to acknowledge the artistic help of Mr. Lawrence Carson, who drew the majority of the illustrations, and to Miss S. Hogue, Miss J. Fontana, Mr. S. Ward and Mr. William R. Dillon who helped in preparing the illustrations. We further acknowledge the help of many other College of San Mateo faculty members.

John C. Williams
Howard C. Monroe

Introduction to the San Francisco Peninsula

Geologic History

Many of the exposed rocks on the San Francisco Peninsula date back more than 180 million years. The major landforms now present are the result of geologic activity during the last 28-30 million years. It was during the geologic period of time known as the Miocene Epoch that the last great inundation of the land by the ocean occurred. This flooding of the lands some 30 million years ago eroded nearly all of the then existing land masses into a great, flat valley which extended almost to present-day Sacramento and Stockton. The Miocene inundation lasted until about 15 million years ago.

As the highlands were worn away, the soils were carried down into the surrounding sea and deposited in broad, flat sedimentary layers. Several isolated islands were formed by the bending, or upwarping of the ocean floor. In that area which is now known as La Honda along Skyline Boulevard, a series of active volcanoes came into existence. During eruptions, both lava and volcanic dust were deposited over the lands and oceans only to settle forming other sedimentary layers. Some of the extruded, molten rock can still be seen in the road cuts near Half Moon Bay, Boulder Creek, and La Honda. All of the sediments which were laid down during this epoch are known collectively as the Monterey Formation.

Near the end of the Miocene Epoch, 15 million years ago, a great compression of the earth's crust occurred which caused a folding of the Monterey sediment into North-South ridges and valleys. Many of the already existing faults such as the San Andreas fault became active, particularly in vertical movement. These cracks in the earth's crust allowed the molten rock trapped below to spew forth onto the surface, and many new volcanoes came into being.

The folding and faulting of the Monterey sediment turned these originally horizontal beds into vertical layers so that those now visible seem to run up and down. The Pinnacles National Monument which is located southeast of Salinas, California, has many startling rock and volcanic formations which were formed during this upheaval about 10 million years ago. The Santa Cruz Mountain Range was pushed up out of the sea near the end of the Miocene upheavals. The Diablo Range, to the east, rose through a similar folding and faulting of the earth's crust. These two ranges were separated by a broad flat plane most of which was still covered by ocean waters. The San Andreas Fault, on the west running under the Santa Cruz Range and the Hayward Fault, to the east, running under the Diablo Range, allowed the lowlands between these two faults to sink, creating a large graben (a sunken area between two raised areas resulting from faulting).

During the early stages of the Pliocene Epoch (10-15 million years ago), erosion surpassed mountain building, and all Bay Area land masses were leveled. One long range of mountains persisted east of the present-day Santa Cruz Range. This ridge of mountains has been called the Orinda-Merced Axis. This ridge extended along the length of the present-day San Francisco Bay from about Sausalito south through San Jose and Hollister.

As the ridges of the Orinda-Merced Axis eroded, their sediments were deposited into the ocean to the west, and into the Central Valley to the east. Many fossils of land plants and animals, including a three-toed horse, can be found in these deposits. These layers of sedimentary rock are called the Purissima Formation. These formations are most apparent at Moss Beach.

As the Pliocene Epoch drew to a close some one million years ago, the Bay Area was again beset by massive folding, warping and faulting. Also, the entire area rose several hundred feet, and the ocean receded far to the west. Part of the ocean's recession was caused by the storage of the waters as ice in continental glaciers. The Santa Cruz Range rose, and extended northward beyond present-day Point Reyes almost to the Russian River.

Climatic conditions during the early Pleistocene (around 800,000 years ago) were favorable for erosion so that the rugged terrain of the late Pliocene was soon eroded into smooth undulating hills. A broad, flat plane again filled the area between the Santa Cruz Ranges and Diablo Ranges. The Sacramento River flowing down from the north through the Great Valley entered this plane south of Napa and flowed to the sea which was then far to the west from its present location. The valley formed by the river separated the Santa Cruz Range to the south from the Marin hills to the north.

The Pleistocene Epoch encompasses the last million years of Bay Area history. During this last epoch, mountains again rose from the lowlands, but this time the mountain building was restricted primarily to fault blocks rising or falling. It was also during this period of time that the later ice ages occurred with their accompanying geologic and climatic effects, and the accompanying ocean level fluctuations.

The San Francisco Bay lowlands dropped toward sea level and broke into blocks. The tops of some of these blocks can still be seen as the Coyote Hills southeast of the San Francisco Bay. The Sacramento River continued to cut down through the fault blocks, eroding away its own river bed on its course to the sea beyond what is now the Golden Gate.

As the huge fault blocks rose up and tilted seaward, they crumbled the rocks between. This crumbled rock eroded away much more rapidly than the more solid blocks, and many parallel valleys resulted. The San Andreas Lake Basin and Crystal Springs Lakes Basins in San Mateo County resulted from such crumbling and erosion. Much of this crumbled rock can still be seen along road cuts in the area of Crystal Springs Lake on the road to Half Moon Bay. At the present time, the San Andreas Fault is moving laterally rather than in its original vertical direction. The western block is moving north along the fault. This huge mass of rock moved northward approximately 12 feet relative to the eastern block during the earthquake of 1906.

The sharp edges and steep slopes of the Coast Range and Santa Cruz Range fault blocks have added greatly to the problem of erosion and landslides. Streams flowing down the sides of these sharp inclines, along with rain run-off during heavy rainy seasons, loosens the poorly compacted soil and whole masses give way.

The melting of the glaciers formed during the last ice age (about 25,000 years ago) resulted in a rise in the ocean level. This caused the flooding of the Sacramento River basin inland to present-day Pittsburg, California. As the waters of the ocean rose, the lowlands between the Santa Cruz Range and the Diablo Range were flooded, and what is now San Francisco Bay came into being.

The completion of the flooding of San Francisco Bay some ten thousand years ago coincided with the coming of man to the Bay region. Since then the level of the Bay has risen and fallen many times, sometimes as much as several hundred feet. This rising and falling of the Bay level still continues as does most of the geological activity which resulted in the formation of the present landscape. (Please see Glen, Hinds, and Zumberge in Appendix #3 for further readings.)

GEOLOGIC TIMETABLE
(In millions of years)

ERA	SPAN	PERIOD	SPAN	EPOCH	SPAN
CENOZOIC	(60-0)	Quaternary	(1-0)	Recent	(12,000 Yrs.)
				Pleistocene	(1-0)
		Tertiary	(60-1)	Pliocene	(15-1)
				Miocene	(30-15)
				Oligocene	(40-30)
				Eocene	(50-40)
				Paleocene	(60-50)
MESOZOIC	(185-60)	Cretaceous	(125-60)		
		Jurassic	(158-125)		
		Triassic	(185-158)		
PALEOZOIC	(550-185)	Permian	(225-185)		
		Pennsylvanian	(270-225)		
		Mississippian	(310-270)	(Carboniferous)	
		Devonian	(355-310)		
		Silurian	(380-355)		
		Ordovician	(450-380)		
		Cambrian	(550-450)		
PRECAMBRIAN	(1,450-550)				
Proterozoic					
Archeozoic					

Weather

The unique weather conditions found in the San Francisco Bay Area, particularly along the San Mateo Peninsula, are caused by several important geological, physical, and meteorological phenomena. Generally speaking, we enjoy a type of weather referred to as "Mediterranean" because of its similarity to the climate in that area of the world. Rather than four distinct seasons, we have only two seasons, a rainy season and a dry season. The temperature in the Bay Area is fairly constant, with much less fluctuation annually than in other parts of the country. Several atmospheric conditions coupled with unique geological features provide a situation conducive to fog, sea breezes, and advection. All of these produce a "greenhouse" effect over much of the peninsula.

Weather may vary so greatly throughout the Bay Area that to attempt a discussion of "Bay Area Weather" would be a grandiose undertaking indeed. Consequently the weather of each different area on the peninsula will be discussed along with the other characteristics of the biome. It will suffice here merely to state the overall controlling factors which make possible this wide range of weather conditions.

Over the Pacific Ocean, somewhere north of the Hawaiian Islands and west of San Francisco, a large, heavy air mass begins to collect during the early spring months. This mass of cool air is called the "Pacific High." Normally, air tends to move outward away from a high pressure zone in all directions toward low pressure zones such as the coast of northern California. However, as this cool air passes eastward, it is affected by the rotation of the earth turning underneath it so that by the time the air mass reaches California, it is moving southeast nearly parallel to the coast. This spinning or swirling effect of air masses due to the earth's rotation is called the "Coriolis Force." There is really no force involved but an effect. The effect results in movement of ocean currents which flow at 45° angles to the main flow of air. This pushes large masses of waters along our coasts.

As the air passes over the Pacific, it absorbs large quantities of water and heat through evaporation from the ocean. This heavily laden air then strikes the coast, and is deflected away as it is piled up seaward by the coast ranges. The buildup of water-saturated air can enter the land areas only through several passes through the mountains, the largest of which is the Golden Gate.

The ocean waters themselves tend to be affected by the Coriolis force of earth's rotation so that cold arctic waters are carried eastward and southward toward the California coast. In the spring, when the Pacific High builds up north of the Hawaiian Islands, the resulting winds rushing

across the ocean's surface push the water before them producing oceanic
currents. This surface displacement of water is compensated for by an
upwelling of cold water from deeper areas so that as the currents flow
past northern California, the water temperature drops drastically, sometimes into the low 50's.

As the water-laden air passes over the chilled ocean waters it is cooled
and its ability to retain the moisture is lessened to the point that condensation occurs. This condensation rushes into the Golden Gate gap in the form
of damp, chilling fog. This cold foggy mist is heavier than the warm air
above it, so it tends to remain close to the surface. During the spring
months, it can be seen pouring down the eastern slopes of the Santa Cruz
Range, through the Crystal Springs gap toward San Mateo, through the San
Bruno gap toward Millbrae and San Bruno, and of course, through the Golden
Gate sometimes under the Golden Gate Bridge obscuring the driver's view
of the Bay, as he drives toward Marin in bright, clear sunshine.

During the early spring and summer months, the increased intensity of
the sun begins to warm the land of the Great Valley which lies between the
coast ranges and the Sierras to the east. As the land warms up, the air
above is also warmed by radiation, causing the air to expand, creating
currents. These currents of warm air move down the western slopes of
the Sierra ranges, across the Great Valley, and over the Diablo Range and
through the Sacramento River gap into the San Francisco Bay Area. The
cool ocean air heavy with its moisture of evaporated ocean and Bay waters
cannot rise above the overlying warm air.

As the cool ocean breezes flow into the Bay Area they begin to pile up
behind (west of) the Diablo Range Buttress. This forces the condensation
layer higher, giving the summers their characteristic high fogs. This
creates a "greenhouse" effect which tends to maintain a relatively constant
temperature from winter, spring, to summer.

San Francisco Bay is a large, shallow body of water. Its ability to ab-
sorb large quantities of radiant heat helps maintain the cool, lower-level
temperatures during the otherwise hot summer months. As the summer
sun shines down into the San Francisco Bay region, evaporation from the
Bay occurs on a huge scale. This cooling evaporation helps retain the cool,
moisture-laden fog ("greenhouse" effect) and, incidentally, our mild summers.

The fall months of October and November are characterized by a drop
in the strength of the Pacific High, and the moisture-laden westerlies. This
allows the hot, dry valley air to penetrate to the coast, and the Bay Area
experiences its "summer", or prolonged "Indian summer".

By the end of November the winter wet season or rainy season has usually begun. This cool-rainy period will last until late February, when the

Pacific Highs again begin to build up north of Hawaii. During the winter months the wind patterns are reversed, bringing warm, moist air into the Bay Area from the South. As the warm moist, oceanic breezes pass over the cooler land masses condensation and rain occur. The rains last until the early spring when the "Pacific High" is re-established to start the annual cycle over again. (Please see Gilliam in Appendix #3 for further readings.)

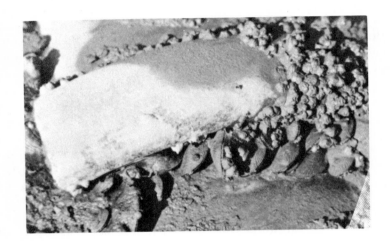

Pipe with Horse mussels and barnacles

Striped Bass

BAY AND SALT MARSH

Introduction to San Francisco Bay and Salt Marshes

San Francisco Bay was formed between ten and twenty-five thousand years ago by the melting of the polar ice caps during the end of the fourth glacial period. As the ocean rose, it flooded through the gap in the coast ranges formed by the Sacramento River at what is now known as the Golden Gate. At that time, there existed a long valley extending north and south between the Santa Cruz Mountains and the Diablo Range from just north of the mouth of the Sacramento River at the Golden Gate to about what is now San Jose. The ocean rose until the banks of the Sacramento River could no longer contain the waters, and a slow inundation of this vast valley between the mountains began.

Near the end of the Pleistocene Epoch some ten thousand years ago, the filling of San Francisco Bay was completed. The filling of the bay roughly corresponds to the coming to the Bay Area of man. As the Bay advanced and receded periodically, the Indian tribes living along the shores moved their settlements accordingly, and the remanents of these settlements can still be found along the hillsides surrounding San Francisco Bay.

Due to the very nature of its origin, San Francisco Bay is a large, shallow body of saline-to-brackish water which is nearly uniform in depth. Its deepest parts are, quite naturally along the route of the old, drowned bed of the Sacramento River as it flowed to the sea west of the Golden Gate. The Bay is still fed daily by the ocean tides coming in from the west, the Sacramento River from the northeast, and Coyote Creek from the south. This causes a daily and sometimes hourly fluctuation in depth, salinity, and temperature throughout the Bay. These environmental fluctuations have their effect upon the animals and plants living within the range of that fluctuation.

It would be a more representative and perhaps more accurate account of the Bay's flora and fauna if each section of the Bay and its surrounding land forms were taken separately, but time and space demands that we attempt to describe just those organisms that might be commonly found throughout the Bay and its shores.

In any field trip to the Bay to see its various areas you may not be able to go to only one place and see all Ecological phenomena. We will discuss each area as one would normally encounter them in a trip to the Bay itself. The four main types of environments to be discussed here are: the marsh lands and their tidal meanders, the shore, the water surface, and its depths. A specific geographic location will be noted for each area, but these are

1

not necessarily the only local areas exemplifying such environments.

The first area usually encountered on foot in a trip to the Bay, will be the Salt Marshes and their tidal meanders. A convenient location which illustrates this area is to be found at the southern end of San Carlos Airport and the surrounding area, and the southeastern fringe of Foster City. Be sure to wear the proper clothing. Old clothes and boots will suffice. A pair of binoculars would be a great help.

Most of the land in this area has been formed by silt settling to the bottom and building layer upon layer. As this sediment accumulates to the maximum of the high tide levels, the waters are excluded in that area. Dust and wind or water moved materials accumulate adding to the further compaction of the soil. The daily tidal fluctuation tends to wear away this build-up of debris in the area of poorest compaction. This erosion of silt creates channels that tend to meander through the marshes, and these channels are called tidal meanders.

As the compacted silt above the high tide level becomes more solid and dryer through evaporation, seeds and other plant materials, born on the winds and other seed dispersal agents such as water, birds, and fecal droppings of other animals, etc., tend to accumulate and grow.

As the salt water evaporates, the salt residue prohibits the growth of all but the most salt-resistant forms of plant life. As these salt-resistant plants grow, their root systems further solidify and hold the accumulating silt. Over periods of years, rain leaches out these salts and allows less-salt-resistant plants to grow in some areas.

General view of Salt Marsh south
of San Carlos, California.

There may be a wide variety of
plants in salt marshes, but only a few
are common to all the San Francisco
Bay salt marshes. Some salt marsh
plants have the ability to excrete any
excess salt taken in from the soil.
Others have the ability to keep salt out
of their root systems.

Salt Grass (*Distichlis spicata*) is a
member of the grass family and displays two distinct forms, the male
plant and the female plant. This condition is known as dioeciousness. The
different sexes are in two different
plants rather than both in the same
plant (monoecious). The stems are
stiff and erect bearing either the male
or the female spike-like flowers in
clumps or bunches at their tips. The
long, narrow typical grass-like leaves
grow out of the stem at intervals giving
a somewhat straggled appearance. The
entire plant may reach a foot in height.

Salt Grass

California Cord Grass (*Spartina
foliosa*) reaches heights in excess of
four feet. Cord Grass is a stout plant
that continues to grow for several seasons, and is a perennial rather than an
annual. Like many marsh plants, it
produces creeping rhizomes or underground stems that act to anchor the
plant in shallow soil as well as spread
the plant by vegetative means. The
leaves are long and narrow. Typical
grass flowers and seeds are produced
on the uppermost spikes of the stems.

The name Pickle-weed (*Salicornia
pacifica*) is appropriate for that marsh
plant for its stems appear to be a series
of long narrow pickles attached end-to-
end. These pickle-like stems branch
opposite to one another and the leaves

California Cord Grass

Pickleweed

Marsh Grindelia

Sand Dock

form scales around the joints of the upper-most segments. This succulent plant may reach a height of 12 inches and, like Cord Grass, is restricted to salt marshes because of its high tolerance to salty and alkaline soils.

Sea Blite (*Suaeda californica*) is a low shrubby plant that grows outward rather than upward. It seldom grows more than a foot in height. The small leaves grow directly out of the stems and the flowers are produced along the stems at the base of the leaves. Sea Blite is a fleshy plant that grows in the more sandy areas of the marshes.

Marsh Grindelia (*Grindelia humilis*) is a broad-leafed, woody plant that reaches a height of about 3 feet. Its leaves are sharply serrated or sawtoothed, gummy, and seem to grow around the stem at the base. The typical yellow Sun Flower is borne on the tip of each stem. This perennial plant is in flower throughout the year.

Marsh Rosemary (*Limonium californicum*) has leaves that are broad and fleshy. Purple flowers are borne in erect bunches or spikes. The entire plant seldom exceeds 2 feet in height.

Hedge Mustard (*Sisymbrium officinale*) is one of the many mustard plants found in the salt marshes. It grows to 4 feet and has branched stems. Seed pods form from small yellow flowers into round 1/2 inch long brown pods that hug the dry stems. The dark green leaves are deeply lobed and hairy, turning purplish as the plant grows older.

For the names of other less common salt marsh plants please check the list at the end of this chapter. Local

changes in environment and the inter-
vention of man may cause a shift in the
distribution of or in the abundance of
these specific plants.

Some of the more common animals
found in these marshy areas are permanent residents of the tidal marshes,
while others are temporary visitors
using the watery low lands as either
summer or winter resting-feeding
areas. We will discuss only those
animals that can usually be seen by
the casual visitor during the majority
of the year. The most obvious animals in the marshes are the birds.

The Marsh Hawk (*Circus cyaneus*)
is a large harrier with a four to eight
foot wingspan that can be seen flying
low over the salt marshes with its narrow, long wings held in a slight "V".
The Marsh Hawks have a white rump
patch and fly with slow wing beats. Its
main diet consists of Salt Marsh Harvest Mice and young rabbits, but Marsh
Hawks do occasionally take small birds.
This is one of the larger birds in the
Bay Area. Nests, made of grasses and
twigs, will usually be found on the
ground.

The Short-eared Owl (*Asio flammeus*)
is another predator of the marsh. This
crow-sized owl is one of the few owls
of California that forages during the
day. It can be distinguished from the
smooth-flying Marsh Hawk by its ir-
regular, slow, almost sloppy flight.
It has a large, blunt head typical of all
owls. Its body and legs are covered
with rusty colored feathers to the feet.
Like the Marsh Hawk, the Short-eared
Owl feeds mostly on small mammals,
and nests on the ground.

Marsh Hawk

Burrowing Owl

Short Eared Owl

Marsh Wren

Common Redwing Blackbird

Western Meadow Lark

The Long-billed Marsh Wren (*Telmatodytes palustris*) is a small bird that may be seen perched on grasses, shrubs, or reeds throughout the salt marshes. It has a slender bill, and a smartly perked up tail. The white stripe over the eye, and the white bars across the back are distinguished field markings. Like all Wrens, the Long-billed Marsh Wren is an insect eater. It builds its nest on the reeds from grasses and leaves.

The Bicolored Redwinged Blackbird (*Agelaius phoeniceus californica*) is a robin-sized bird that is jet black with the exception of the bright red epaulets, or shoulder markings. It is distinguished from the common Redwing Blackbird (*Agelaius phoeniceus*) by the absence of the yellow stripe just under the red epaulet. These birds are primarily seed eaters, but will eat nearly anything palatable. They can be seen perched on the top of salt bushes swaying in the breeze occasionally giving out with their raucous cry. These birds nest in the Cattails bordering the water courses and shores in the Bay Area and they also nest in the reeds around the Crystal Springs Lakes.

Another robin-sized bird is the Western Meadow Lark, (*Sturnella neglecta*). This colorful bird is easily identified by the bright yellow throat and breast and distinctive black V-shaped bib. Its back, tail, head, and wings are dusty, striped brown. The characteristic Meadow Lark song is very familiar to anyone who spends time in open areas or fields in the Bay Area. The Meadow Lark is an omnivore eating both seeds and insects.

The typical Meadow Lark nest is a small grassy depression placed on the ground.

The predominant large mammal in the salt marsh area is the Black-tailed Jack Rabbit (*Lepus californicus*). This wiry hare (not a true rabbit) may reach lengths up to two feet and weigh in excess of six pounds. Its long, powerful legs and quick reflexes make the Jack Rabbit one of the fastest animals and provides excellent sport for the Bobcats, Cougars, large hawks and man. In areas where the owls and other predators have been removed, the Jack Rabbit can become a serious pest. Each female may have as many as three litters a year with each litter yielding six to eight young. Nearly any low grassy or shrubby plant is food for the Jack.

Another smaller mammal occasionally seen in the Bay Area marshes is the Brush Rabbit (*Sylvilagus bachmani*). The Brush Rabbit is a small cottontail that usually inhabits the woodlands or chaparral. They can sometimes be seen darting through their weed-covered trails along the edges of salt marshes. This animal seldom exceeds one foot in length with short, rounded ears (about 2 and a half inches long). It is somewhat darker than the typical cotton-tail of the grasslands, but eats generally the same foods, namely grasses and roots of small plants. The primary predators on this animal in the salt marshes are the Marsh Hawks and the Short-eared Owl.

Other small mammals include the Salt Marsh Harvest Mouse (*Reithrodontomys raviventris*), Shrews and of

California Jack Rabbit

Brush Rabbit

Harvest Mouse

Norway Rat

course Rats. The Shrews will be discussed in later chapters. Much could be written about the rodents, but because most of the large rats are "imports" and not really native to this area they will be excluded.

The small 2 1/2 to 3 1/2 inch brown Harvest Mouse lives among the grasses, cord grass and pickleweed of the salt marsh. It eats primarily the seeds of the plants in which it burrows and nests. This rodent serves as a major source of food for the Short-eared Owls and other predators.

In this same area we usually find tidal channels or meanders with slowly flowing waters. Along the edges of these channels we will find many types of birds either foraging or resting. The main birds common to the San Francisco Bay tidal meanders are of four types; fish eaters such as Herons, Egrets and Terns; invertebrate eaters (snails, clams, worms) such as Willets, Curlews, and Avocets; filter feeders such as the ducks; and finally the scavengers like the Sea Gulls.

The Common or American Egret (*Casmerodius albus*) is a large (three to four foot) white bird with long legs, usually a curved snake-like neck and a long black-tipped yellow bill. This bird forages along the edges of the meanders making quick stabbing motions with its beak at small fish. When disturbed the Egrets take to flight, on long broad wings, with a slow flapping motion. Their neck and feet are extended while in flight. The Egret nest, like the Heron's, is placed high in trees whenever possible. This bird is a winter visitor to California but some can be found here during all seasons.

Another Egret is the Snowy Egret (*Leucophoyx thula*) which is about half the size of the Common Egret. It has white feathers, and a long, narrow black bill. These birds eat crabs,

American Egret

shrimp, small fish, and other invertebrates. These birds also nest in trees,
shrubs or in reeds. The nest is made
out of sticks, and matted vegetation.
Four or five small, pale blue-green
eggs are laid in the spring. Many of
these Egrets and Herons breed in rook-
eries on "Land islands" in Marin County
and in trees at Pescadero Creek in
Southern San Mateo County.

Another fish-eating bird is the Great
Blue Heron (*Ardea herodias*). This
bird will also include many other animals in its diet. It has been seen eating snakes, frogs, small birds, insects, and other marsh animals. Most
of the fish eaten by this bird are of the
non-game fishes variety and the removal of these "Garbage" fish often
increases the productivity of this area
for game fish. The large, four foot,
heron is bluish-grey in color with a
whitish head and neck. This bird also
has a yellowish bill. Heron nest in the
upper branches of trees, building large
nests of twigs and leaves. Like the
Egret, this bird flies with a slow flapping of the wings, but withdraws its
head between its shoulders while in
flight.

The Western Grebe (*Aechmophorus
occidentalis*) depends almost entirely
upon small fish for its food. This is
perhaps the largest grebe found in our
area. Its total length may exceed 2
feet and the wingspan will often be 3
feet or more. This Grebe is characterized by a long, slender white neck
and a dark grey body. It has a yellow,
slender, slightly up-turned bill. Grebe
nests are large floating masses of

Snowy Egret

Great Blue Heron

Western Grebe

Pied-billed Grebe

Forester's Tern

Caspian Tern

Willet

weeds and other marsh vegetation anchored in the reeds. This bird is primarily a winter visitor.

Several other grebes are residents in the bay area. Among these are the Pied-billed Grebe, and the Eared Grebe.

Two smaller fish-eaters are the Forster's Tern and the Caspian Tern. The Forster's Tern (*Sterna forsteri*) is a small (12-16") black-capped tern with an orange black-tipped bill. The terns have the characteristic "V" notched tail which is visible when they are soaring. These birds are white below and light grey above.

The last fish-eating bird to be mentioned is the Caspian Tern (*Hydroprogne caspia*). This is a much larger bird, about crow size. It is white with a black "cap" on its head. It has a large, thick, red bill. These birds can be differentiated from the gulls when in flight by the moderately forked tail and black "cap." The terns usually forage by flying 25-30 feet over the water and peering downward until a fish is seen. When the prey is seen the tern immediately folds its wings and dives headlong into the water seizing the fish with its bill. The tern almost immediately takes to the air again. Terns rarely nest in the Bay Area. Their primary nesting areas are along bays and lakes in the far North (Oregon through Southern Alaska and Canada).

The invertebrate-eating birds are much more numerous than the larger fish-eaters. One of the most obvious and common is the Willet (*Catoptrophorus semipalmatus*). This long-legged shore bird is a non-descript grey when walking along tidal meanders, but when in flight it displays beautiful white wing flashes. The Willet uses its long, narrow, blackish bill to probe into the mud for worms, snails, clams, and other invertebrates. The body of this bird is about the size of a stream-lined pigeon.

Other shore birds found in the San Francisco Bay tidal areas are the Curlews. The Long-billed Curlew (*Numenius americanus*) is a Willet-sized brownish shore bird and may be seen walking in shallow water on its long, thin legs poking its long, slender, down-curved bill into the bottom mud for crustaceans and other invertebrates.

The Hudsonian Curlew (*Numenius phaeopus*) is a smaller bird with a shorter, down-curved bill. Unlike the Long-billed Curlew, the Hudsonian Curlew or Whimbrel is greyish-brown with a striped head. Both birds are migrants and can be seen during their North-South migration.

The Avocet (*Recurvirostra americana*) is one of the prettiest shore birds found in our salt marshes. It moves its white, black and reddish-brown body through the shallows on long, thin, bluish legs. The Avocet is about 18 inches tall, has a 2 1/2 foot wing span, and when flying, the legs are held straight out behind the bird. Its very slender bill is blackish and up-turned, and is used to probe in the mud flats for food. The Avocet and the following shore birds use their long, slender bills to probe down into the soft, organic, ooze capturing small invertebrates. In gut analysis of these birds, we found primarily mud, broken shells, arthropod

Long-billed Curlew

Hudsonian Curlew

American Avocet

appendages and worms. Few intact animals or shells were found with the exception of a small, red worm. Whether or not these birds extract nutrients from the organic ooze itself is not known.

The only other bird in the marshes with an up-turned bill is the Marbled Godwit (*Limosa fedoa*) which is about the same size as the Avocet, but the Godwit is a mottled brown. The short-billed Dowitcher (*Limnodromus griseus*) looks like a small (12 inch tall) Marbled Godwit. It has a rusty brown body, shorter legs, and a shorter, uniformly straight grey bill. The Black-necked Stilt (*Himantopus mexicanus*) also has a black and white pattern, but its wings are solid black and its legs are red. It is slightly smaller than the Avocet or Godwit. The Black-necked Stilt and the Avocet are the only two shorebirds that nest in San Francisco Bay. All others breed in or near the Arctic. Many other small birds are found on the tidal mud flats. For a comprehensive description of these birds, please check the references at the end of this chapter.

Marbled Godwit

Black-necked Stilt

Dowitcher

You will find the following birds on
the water's surface of these tidal meanders and occasionally on the land
where they rest and feed.

The Shoveler (*Spatula clypeata*) is a
small duck (18-20 inches) with a long,
broad bill. This bird is typical of the
dabbling ducks which feed on the surface by upending themselves. The
edges of the Shoveler's bill are lined
with hair-like projections that filter
plankton from the waters. This is one
of the most common ducks of the salt
evaporators, feeding on the large numbers of Brine Shrimp (*Artemia salina*)
common to those areas. Male Shovelers
have a green head and tail, with a white
chest and rump, and reddish sides.
The females are mottled brown with a
blue shoulder patch.

Shoveler

The Mallard (*Anas platyrhynchos*)
is another of the more common dabbling ducks to be found in the marshes
and on the waters of the bay. The male
Mallard is a beautiful bird having a
greenish head with a white stripe around
its neck. Its ruddy colored breast and
white tail, which is topped by several
curled feathers, give this bird a distinctive appearance. The Mallard is
one of our largest ducks and may have
a three foot wingspan. The Mallard,
like most dabbling ducks, explodes
vertically into flight.

Brine Shrimp

Mallard

Unlike most of our bay waterfowl,
Mallards are residents of the San
Francisco Bay region, and can be seen
in harbors, parks, and ponds, as well
as in the salt marshes year round.
Their nests are composed of grasses
placed in hollows on the ground in dense
weeds. The Mallard female lays many

eggs (up to 10 per clutch). Its food consists primarily of plant material such as seeds, grasses and marine algae, but it can feed by upending itself in the water and filtering its food from the bottom ooze.

The Canvas-back (*Aythya valisineria*), unlike the Mallard, breeds in Canada and spends only the winters in the Bay Area. Its white back, rusty red head and neck, and black breast and tail sets the male Canvas-back apart from other ducks on the Bay. The females of this species follow the general rule among ducks, donning themselves with drabber colors than their male counterparts. This is a diving duck feeding upon roots, stems, and other plant materials, but they may also take small fish or crustaceans. The Canvas-back, like most diving ducks, must run upon the water to gain flight speed. When migrating they fly in distinctive "V" shaped formation with rapid wing beats.

A similar, but slightly smaller, bird is the Redhead (*Aythya americana*). The primary difference is its high, distinctively rounded forehead as contrasted with the sloping forehead of the Canvas-back. The Redhead has a 20-inch body and a 30-inch wingspan while the Canvas-back is slightly larger. Redheads are also diving ducks with similar food preferences, but they differ in their migratory flight pattern. The Redhead flies as a single bird not in large flocks.

The Lesser Scaup (*Aythya affinis*) is perhaps the most common migrant duck. Both the Lesser and Greater Scaups are very common on the tidal meanders where they filter debris from the

Canvas-back

Redhead Duck

bottom. These birds from a distance
appear blackish at both ends and white
in the middle. The Lesser Scaup has
a purplish head while the Greater Scaup
(*Aythya marila*) has a greenish head.
Both are diving ducks.

The last group of birds to be discussed will be the scavengers. The
primary scavengers of the Bay and
Marshes are the Sea Gulls. All of the
sea gulls are good swimmers and will
eat nearly anything living or dead that
floats on or just beneath the surface of
the water. This makes these birds
important as scavengers in our environment. They carry out the function
performed by Vultures and Crows of
the terrestrial habitat. This scavenging is a necessary part of the ecological
system and therefore these birds are
protected by law.

Greater Scaup   (left)

Lesser Scaup   (right)

Their feet are large and webbed,
giving their land ambuling an awkward
wobble. The novice viewing gulls for
the first time seeing them see-saw back
and forth as they make their way on foot
may conclude that these large white
birds are ungainly. One has only to
spend a few minutes along the coast
observing the gulls riding the up-drafts
on their beautifully curved wings, seldom resorting to flapping, to be con-
vinced of their superior airmanship.
The flights of few birds have inspired
as much poetry or music as that of the
gull.

The Western Gull (*Larus occidentalis*)
is perhaps the most common gull found
along the salt marshes of San Francisco
Bay. Like nearly all of the gulls seen
here, it is a large bird, measuring up
to two feet in length with long wings.

The Western Gull is a resident of this
area, and may be observed on our bay
year round. It may be difficult at first
for the casual observer to notice the
difference between the various gulls.
The Western Gull has pink feet and a
very dark gray mantle (area composed
of the upper wings and part of the back
between the wings). The head, body,
and tail are a uniform white. The
yellow bill has a red spot on the lower
part. The California Gull (*Larus californicus*) is similar only its mantle is
a lighter gray, with black wingtips
which show a white spot or "mirror"
along the leading edge. The California
Gull also has greenish feet and a red
or red and black spot on the lower
mandible of its bill. The Herring
Gull (*Larus argentatus*) is similar in
general coloration to the California
Gull, but this gull has flesh-colored
legs and a red spot on the bill. The
Heerman's Gull (*Larus heermanni*) is
dark gray with a white head, red bill,
black feet, and a black tail.

Leaving the tidal marshes, and pro-
ceeding toward the bay proper we encounter the third ecological unit of the
bay. This is the shoreline of the bay
itself. Here we have still another set
of ecological factors. This area is
open, windswept and more susceptible
to wave and tidal action. There are
few plants along the water's edge, and
animal life is restricted primarily to
invertebrates and the birds that feed
upon them. We will reserve the descriptions of the marine invertebrates
for the chapter dealing with the open
coast.

Herring Gull

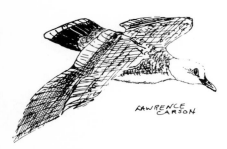

Heermann's Gull

Many of the birds of the tidal meanders will also be found foraging or
resting on the intertidal areas of the
bay edge. Such birds as the Willets,
Curlews, Marbled Godwit, Avocets,
and the Gulls are common here. Swarms
of Sanderlings, Black-bellied Plovers,
and Killdeer may also be found feeding
here.

Sanderlings

The Sanderlings (*Crocethia alba*) are
among the smallest of the birds to be
found wading along the edges of the
Bay. This shorebird is about sparrow-
sized. It is rusty brown with distinctive white wing markings that can be
seen when it is in flight. The Sander-
ling usually feeds on crustaceans and
snails found in the mud or shallow
waters. When flying, a high pitched
"kip kip" can be heard. Whole flocks
of twenty to forty of these small birds
may be seen running and stopping,
feeding, then running again almost in
unison. Their flight is rapid and usually low over the water.

Black-bellied Plover

The Black-bellied Plover (*Squatarola
squatarola*) is the size of a robin. It
has a very distinctive black face, throat,
and belly with white markings through
the eyes and down both sides of the
neck. The back and wings of this bird
are mottled gray. Like other shore
birds, they probe in the shallows and
along the mudflats for invertebrates.

The Killdeer (*Charadrius vociferus*)
is another robin-sized shore bird that
is found along the shores of the Pacific
Ocean and in nearly every bay, estuary,
dry creek bed, and field. It is perhaps
the most widely distributed of the shore
birds. This plover is distinguished by
its white breast with two distinct black

Killdeer

bands running across it, as well as its "kill-deer" call which it voices when in flight. Killdeer eat seeds, insects, and other small invertebrates.

Knots, Yellow Legs, several other Plovers, various Sandpipers, and many types of ducks and geese are migratory passing through our area during the Spring and Fall. For identification of these birds please see appropriate references.

The last ecological unit of the bay to be encountered is the water itself. We shall include both the surface and subsurface parts of the bay in this section.

Many different marine invertebrates live in the bay. These include various types of plankton, larger crustaceans, worms, and mollusks. Many vertebrate organisms live here feeding on smaller vertebrates and invertebrates. Most of these organisms are very secretive or at least not obvious, and most people know very little about these strange looking creatures. The chapter on the "Open Coast" will cover many of these so we will defer discussion of all but the most obvious organisms of the bay itself until a later time.

Two large fish-eating birds are common to our bay, and are also very obvious. They are the Cormorants and the Pelicans.

The Double-crested Cormorant (*Phalacocorax auritus*) is a long-necked bird, that is almost entirely black with the exceptions of a yellow patch beneath the lower bill and, during the breeding season, white tufts of feathers behind the eyes. This Cormorant is about gull-sized, but much slimmer

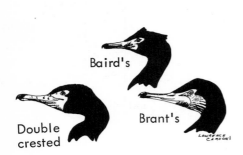

Baird's

Double crested

Brant's

Cormorant

Bairds Cormorant

and with a distinctive snake-like neck. Cormorants feed by diving under water and chasing their fish prey. Some of these birds have been trained by oriental fishermen serving quite well as long as a string is tied around the Cormorant's throat to prevent the bird from swallowing its catch. Cormorants build their nest in trees or on open coastal rocks out of twigs or seaweed.

Brown Pelican

The largest fish-eating bird on the bay is the California Brown Pelican (*Pelecanus occidentalis californicus*). Its wingspread may exceed six feet. Any flock of large, heavy birds flying in a long string or loose "V", alternating several slow wing beats with long glides, will usually turn out to be pelicans. Darker such birds will be the California Brown Pelican while white birds exhibiting these flight characteristics are the larger (90-inch wingspan) White Pelican (*Pelecanus erythrorhynchos*). White Pelicans are more common on the open coast. Pelicans feed by diving from about 20 feet headlong into the water after fish close to the surface. Brown Pelicans nest along our coast, while the White Pelicans nest primarily in Nevada and Utah. Most of our ducks are temporary visitors to the Bay Area. They are seasonal or rare and therefore will not be discussed in detail in this chapter. However, a check list of most of these birds is provided for reference purposes at the end of this chapter.

White Pelican

Baldpate

Coot

Canada Goose

Green-winged Teal

White-winged Scoter

Brant

Many types of fish are found in the San Francisco Bay. The following are but a few of the more interesting and exciting examples.

The Striped Bass (*Roccus saxatilis*) is a member of the Bass family that was brought into San Francisco Bay in 1879. It is an excellent game fish, and provides a very tasty dinner. Stripers prefer sandy or rocky bottoms, and are in greatest abundance in the northern reaches of San Francisco and San Pablo Bay, but are caught off Coyote Point. These fish may exceed 100 pounds in weight, and will grow to five feet in length, but 20-pounders are much more common. The Striped Bass move into fresh water in the San Joaquin Delta during the winter months and then spawn there in April and May. The summer months are usually spent in the salty bay waters and occasionally in the open ocean near the Golden Gate.

Striped Bass

The Diamond Turbot (*Hypsopsetta guttulata*) is a flat fish that as an adult has both of its eyes on the right side of its head. The upper, or right, side of the body has a uniform greenish appearance. The underside, or left side, is usually yellowish-white with a yellow marking around the mouth. This small flat fish seldom reaches a length of 15 inches, and usually weighs less than two pounds. Its tough skin hides a tasty flesh although some have a slight iodine flavor.

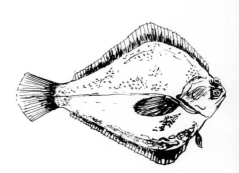

Diamond Turbot

The Starry Flounder (*Platichthys stellatus*) may reach a weight of 20 pounds and a length of three feet which makes it the largest of our flat fish. It is easily distinguished from the other flounders by the black alternating

Flounder

stripes running parallel with the rays of the Dorsal, Ventral, and Caudal fins. The upper side is covered by dark splotches of scales separated by smooth scale-free skin. As with all flounders, both eyes are on the upper side (right or left), and the lower side is plain whitish in color. This animal makes excellent eating, and is sold on the open market as fillet of sole. Most flatfish tend to bury themselves in the sand as a means of self protection as they are poor swimmers. They also use this concealment as a means of surprising their prey which consists of crustaceans, worms, and small fish.

Several kinds of perch are found in San Francisco Bay. One of the most common is the Shiner Perch (*Cymatogaster aggregata*). This fish, like most Surfperch, has a broad, flattened body similar to the fresh water "Sunfish" or "Bluegill." The Shiner Perch reaches about 6 inches in length. They are silvery, but the males may have black horizontal side stripes during the breeding season. These fish are commonly caught off Coyote Point, Foster City, and the San Mateo-Hayward Bridge.

The Black Perch (*Embiotoca Jacksoni*) is similar in body shape, but is larger (up to 14 inches), and is usually darker. However, the coloration of this fish is quite variable and may be blue, brown, red, and/or yellow. These perch are most often caught around rocks or pilings in the Bay. Both of these perch are good to eat, and are usually caught on live or cut bait.

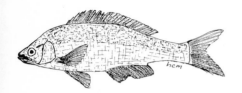

Shiner Perch

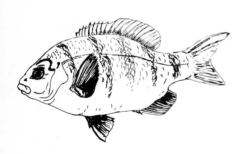

Black Perch

The Mudsucker (*Gillichthys mira-bilis*) is perhaps the most common fish of the salt evaporators, sloughs, and mudflats of San Francisco Bay. This fish seldom exceeds 8 inches in length. It has a long narrow body that is dark brown or greenish-brown with dots or bars. Mudsuckers serve as food for the Herons, Egrets, and Mergansers.

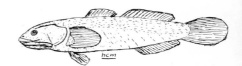

Mudsucker

The Lingcod (*Ophiodor elongetus girard*) is not a true codfish. This rather ugly fish has many large, sharp teeth in its mouth, and sharp tooth-like structures on the inside of the gill cover. Full rows of spines support its two dorsal fins. It is an excellent game fish, and reaches lengths up to four feet and weighs in excess of 70 pounds. Its dark, sometimes blue-green, flesh is quite edible when properly prepared.

Lingcod

There are two species of Sturgeon indigenous to the Bay and both are anadromous (marine fish that enter fresh water to spawn). The White Sturgeon (*Acipenser transmontanus*) is larger than the Green Sturgeon (*Acipenser medirostris*). The White Sturgeon, which may exceed nine feet in length, is greyish-brown with broad flat, primitive ganoid scales, forming rows of plates along the back and sides. The head of this fish is flattened top to bottom and has a long, pointed snout protruding forward, and above the wide sucker-like mouth. The Green Sturgeon is green, and smaller (about four feet) with a more pointed snout. The row, or eggs, from Sturgeons is made into cavier, and the flesh is quite tasty.

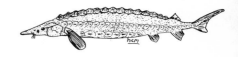

White Sturgeon

The Brown Smoothhound Shark (*Rhinotriacis henlei gill*) is the most abundant shark in San Francisco Bay.

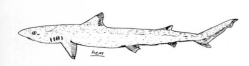

Female Brown Smoothhound Shark

Female Dogfish Shark

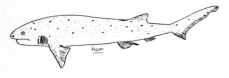

Male Sevengill Cowshark

Its even, brownish, rusty-colored upper surface and white belly distinguishes this small, cartilagenous fish. The flesh of the Brown Smoothhound is very good to eat, and is among the tastiest of shark meat. It seldom exceeds 36 inches in length and offers excellent sport fishing on light to medium tackle. This shark, like all sharks, has a distinctive type of minute (placoid) scale that feels smooth when rubbed from head to tail but is rough when rubbed from tail to head.

(*Squalus acanthias linneaus*) the Dogfish Shark, reaches about five feet in length and usually swims in large schools. Dogfish Sharks are uniformly gray on their dorsal surface and white along their ventral surface. In the past, this fish served as an important source of Vitamin A, but now that function has been taken over by the synthetic drug industry. Their ecological function, however, remains the same. It is a scavenging predator, and in turn it provides food for larger sharks and bigger, faster fish. The meat of the Dogfish Shark is white and quite good to eat particularly when broiled in butter with lemon slices. One word of caution should be said regarding the hard, sharp spines found along the leading edge of each of the two dorsal fins. These spines can inflict a very painful wound if the fish is handled carelessly when being boated. The Dogfish Shark gives birth to live young which are quite capable of fending for themselves at birth.

The Sevengill Cowshark (*Notorynchus maculatum ayres*) is probably the largest shark found in the San Francisco

Bay. While the largest recorded catch
is about 8 1/2 feet, these sharks are
reputed to reach 15 feet in length. The
Sevengill Cowshark as the name implies, has seven gill slits along each
side of its neck region, and only one
dorsal fin set well back near the tail.
The flesh is edible, and is sold on the
open market. This shark, like most of
the sharks of the bay, feeds on small
fish, and other animals found on or
near the bottom.

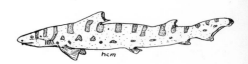

Female Leopard Shark

The Leopard Shark (*Triakis semifasciata girard*) is perhaps the most
attractive shark found in our waters.
It is light gray with dark bars and spots
arranged evenly along the dorsal surface and sides. Its belly is pale gray
and lacks markings. The Leopard
Shark is quite sporting on light tackle
and the flesh is tasty. These sharks
rarely grow to more than four feet in
length. The sex of all sharks and rays
can be determined very easily from external observations. If there are two
long projections (called claspers) extending from the pelvic fins next to the
body then the shark or ray is a male.
If there is only normal pelvic fins without lobes or projections then you have a
female animal. None of the sharks
normally found in the bay are dangerous to man.

Bat Ray and Leopard Shark

One of the largest and most bizarre
fish found in the bay is the Bat Ray
(*Myliobatis californicus*). It reaches
a weight in excess of 200 pounds, and
usually travels in large groups. Its
typical sting ray characteristics are
augmented by a large blunt head with
bulging eyes. The pectoral fins, which
make up the "wings," are sharply

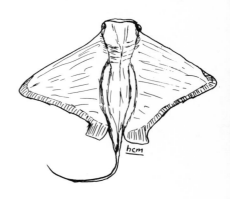

Female Bat Ray

Round Stingray

Guitarfish

pointed and the fish uses them to "fly" through the water by a flapping motion. The long, slender tail has no caudal fin, but does have a large stinger embedded near its base. These animals are quite harmless if handled carefully. They feed on clams, worms, and other bottom-living organisms.

The last animal to be mentioned in this chapter is also a ray. The Round Stingray (*Urolophus halleri*) is the only Stingray found in these waters that possesses a true caudal fin on its tail. The Round Stingray seldom exceeds 15 inches in length, and its body is almost circular when viewed from above. The leading edge of the pectoral fin extends forward out in front of the head and forms a slight point separating the dorsal from the ventral surfaces. These are bottom-dwelling animals that also possess a stinger in the base of their tails. These stingers can inflict a very painful wound if the fish is stepped upon or handled carelessly.

Many other types of small fishes can be found in the bay. A check list of the more obvious fishes will be added at the end of this chapter. Most of the organisms on this list have been covered in some detail in this chapter but not all.

A Checklist of Coastal and Bay
Salt Marsh Plants and Animals

Those with the asterisks are mentioned in this chapter.

Plants

* Saltgrass (*Distichlis spicata*)
* Pickleweed (*Salicornia pacifica*)
* Sea Blite (*Suaeda californica*)
* Marsh Rosemary (*Limonium californicum*)
* California Cord Grass (*Spartina foliosa*)
* Marsh Grindelia (*Grindelia humilis*)
* Hedge Mustard (*Sisymbrium officinale*)
  Salt Brush (*Atriplex leucophylla*)
  Wild Mustard (*Brassica spp.*)
  Cattail (*Typha angustifolia*)
  Star Thistle (*Centaurea solstitialis*)
  Sweet Anise (*Foeniculum vulgare*)
  Marsh Dodder (*Cuscuta salina*)
  Docks (*Rumex spp.*)
  Jaumea (*Jaumea carnosa*)
  Wild Oats (*Avena fatua*)

Animals
Mammals

* Black-tailed Jack Rabbit (*Lepus californicus*)
* Brush Rabbit (*Sylvilagus bachmani*)
* Salt-Marsh Harvest Mouse (*Reithrodontomys raviventris*)
  Vagrant Shrew (*Sorex vagrans*)
  Trowbridge Shrew (*Sorex trowbridgii*)
  Norway Rat (*Rattus norvegicus*)
  Black Rat (*Rattus rattus*)

Birds

  Burrowing Owl (*Speotyto cunicularia*)
* Marsh Hawk (*Circus cyaneus*)
* Short-eared Owl (*Asio flammeus*)
* Black Brant (*Branta nigricans*)
* Long-billed Marsh Wren (*Telmatodytes palustris*)

Birds (continued)

* Bicolored Redwinged Black Bird (*Agelaius phoeniceus californica*)
* Common Redwing Black Bird (*A. phoeniceus*)
* Western Meadow Lark (*Sturnella neglecta*)
* Common Egret (*Casmerodius albus*)
* Great Blue Heron (*Ardea herodias*)
  Clapper Rail (*Rallus longirostris*)
* Western Grebe (*Aechmophorus occidentalis*)
* Forster Tern (*Sterna forsteri*)
* Caspian Tern (*Hydroprogne caspia*)
* Willet (*Catoptrophorus semipalmatus*)
* Long-billed Curlew (*Numenius americanus*)
* Hudsonian Curlew (*Numenius phaeopus*)
  White-winged Scoter (*Melanitta deglandi*)
* Snowy Egret (*Leucophoyx thula*)
* Dowitcher (*Limnodromus griseus*)
* Avocet (*Recurvirostra americana*)
* Marbled Godwit (*Limosa fedoa*)
* Black-necked Stilt (*Himantopus mexicanus*)
  White-tailed Kite (*Elanus leucurus*)
* Shoveler (*Spatula clypeata*)
* Mallard (*Anas platyrhynchos*)
* Canvas-back (*Aythya valisineria*)
* Lesser Scaup (*Aythya affinis*)
* Greater Scaup (*Aythya marila*)
* Redhead (*Aythya americana*)
* Western Gull (*Larus occidentalis*)
* California Gull (*Larus californicus*)
* Herring Gull (*Larus argentatus*)
* Heerman's Gull (*Larus heermanni*)
* Sanderlings (*Crocethia alba*)
  Pintail (*Anas acuta*)
  Bufflehead (*Bucephala albeola*)
* Black-bellied Plover (*Squatarola squatarola*)
* Killdeer (*Charadrius vociferus*)
  Surf Scoter (*Melanitta perspicillata*)
  Gadwall (*Anas strepera*)
  Ruddy Duck (*Oxyura jamaicensis*)
  Blue-winged Teal (*Anas discors*)
* Double-crested Cormorant (*Phalacrocorax auritus*)
* California Brown Pelican (*Pelecanus occidentalis californicus*)

Birds (continued)

* White Pelican (*Pelecanus erythrorhynchos*)
  Western Sandpiper (*Ereunetes mauri*)
  Canada Goose (*Branta canadensis*)
  White-fronted Goose (*Anser albifrons*)
  Cinnamon Teal (*Anas cyanoptera*)
  Baldpate (*Mareca americana*)
  Wood-duck (*Aix sponsa*)
  Pacific Loon (*Gavia arctica*)
  Pied-billed Grebe (*Podilymbus podiceps*)
  Green Wing Teal (*Anas carolinensis*)
  Brant (*Branta bernicla*)
  Blue-throat Brandt's Cormorant (*Phalacrocorax penicillatus*)
  Red-throat Baird's Cormorant (*Phalacrocorax pelagicus*)

Fish

* Striped Bass (*Roccus saxatilis*)
* Diamond Turbot (*Hypsopsetta guttulata*)
* Starry Flounder (*Platichthys stellatus*)
* Shiner Perch (*Cymatogaster aggregata*)
* Black Perch (*Embiotoca jacksoni*)
* Mudsucker (*Gillichthys mirabilis*)
* Lingcod (*Ophiodor elongetus girard*)
* White Sturgeon (*Acipenser transmontanus*)
* Green Sturgeon (*Acipenser medirostris*)
* Brown Smoothhound Shark (*Rhinotriacis henlei gill*)
* Dogfish Shark (*Squalus acanthias linneaus*)
* Sevengill Cowshark (*Notorynchus maculatum ayres*)
* Leopard Shark (*Triakis semifasciata girard*)
* Bat Ray (*Myliobatis californicus*)
* Round Stingray (*Urolophus halleri*)
  Shovelnose Guitar (*Rhinobatos productus*)

Invertebrates

  Bay mussels (*Mytilus edulis*)
  Horse mussel (*Volsella demissa*)(*Modiolus*)
  Eastern oysters (*Crassostrea virginica*)
  Catspaw oyster (*Ostrea lurida*)

Invertebrates (continued)

Pill Bug   (*Idothea urotoma*)
Dog whelk   (*Ilyanassa obsoleta*)
Channeled whelk   (*Busycon canaliculatus*)
Limpets   (*Acmaea spp.*)
Barnacles   (*Balanus spp.*)
Bay Rock crab   (*Hemigrapsus oregonensis*)
Pacific oyster   (*Crassostrea gigas*)
Atlantic drill   (*Urosalpinx cinereus*)
Brackish water crab   (*Rhithropanopeus harrisi*)
Eastern soft shell clam   (*Mya arenaria*)
Brackish water shrimp   (*Palaemon macrodactylus*)
Japanese "littleneck" clam   (*Protothaca semidecussata*)
Bent nose clam   (*Macoma nasuta*)
The wondering sponge   (*Tetilla mutabilis*)
The Sea Pen   (*Acanthoptilum gracile*)
Jackknife clam   (*Tagelus californianus*)
The Blue Mud shrimp   (*Upogebia pugettensis*)
The Rough piddock   (*Zirfaea pilsbryi*)
The Ghost shrimp   (*Callianassa spp.*)
Brine shrimp   (*Artemia salina*)

Black Perch

Name _____

Score _____

Field Exercise #1

Plants

List the common endemic plants observed on your field trip.

1.   6.

2.   7.

3.   8.

4.   9.

5.   10.

Animals

List the common endemic animals seen on your field trip.

Invertebrates   Birds – Residents   Birds – Migrants

1.   1.   1.

2.   2.   2.

3.   3.   3.

4.   4.   4.

5.   5.   5.

6.   6.   6.

7.   7.   7.

8.   8.   8.

9.   9.   9.

10.   10.   10.

Mammals

1.

2.

3.

4.

5.

Field Exercise #2   Name_____

                                     Score_____

Write a short essay describing the habitat, environmental factors, and niche of any animal endemic to this area.

THE OPEN COAST

The next area to be discussed is the exposed rocky coast. The following description can be used specifically for the coast from Pillar Point, Princeton, California to Montara Point, California. Similar plants, animals, geology, and weather conditions can be found from Mendocino County south through Morro Bay. Be sure to visit the beach at low tide or the plants and animals will be covered with water. Tide books are available at most local sporting goods stores. Be sure to take the proper equipment such as rubber soled boots, a pail, a knife, a geology pick or hammer, and warm, dry clothing. Also be careful, for the wet rocks are slippery.

The exposed road cuts along the coast highway between Devil's Slide to the North, and Moss Beach to the South are principally Cretaceous sandstone and shale. This material was deposited beneath the ocean during the last half of the Mesozoic Era (about 100 million years ago).

The road cuts between Pedro Point and Devil's Slide expose early Cenozoic shale and sandstone. This sedimentary rock was deposited some 50 to 70 million years ago as a bottom to the ocean that had again flooded the lands inland beyond the present day great valley.

All of the strata visible at Seal Cove are of the Purissima formation laid down during the middle or early Pliocene epoch some 10 to 15 million years ago. All of the sedimentary rock beds on the floor of Moss Beach itself are also of the Purissima formation. In the middle Cretaceous period of the Mesozoic Era (100 million years ago), a huge magma intrusion which is now called Montara Mountain welled up in its present location. This magma cooled into granite. During the weathering periods of the Pliocene epoch (10 million years ago) the overlying rocks were worn away and were deposited along the coast forming the present Purissima formation.

The concentric ring-like structures shaped by the rock strata on the floor of Moss Beach form what is known as the "Moss Beach Syncline." Due to increasing pressures above and/or to the sides of this area, the bottom began to sink or "sag", bending the layers of deposited materials above downward into a bowl shape. Later, as the lands rose up and were worn away, the various layers were exposed creating the coliseum effect visible from the surrounding cliffs. These cliffs were deposited much later, probably less than one million years ago.

The climate along the coast is controlled by moist winds blowing on shore from the ocean. This condition keeps the temperature from fluctuating very much from day to night or from season to season. There is little difference in the seasons. The summers are cool and the winters are a bit warmer. Fog is prevalent both seasons. The day may start out

foggy and change to a beautiful sunny day and then change abruptly to a
cold misty afternoon or evening. Be prepared for these changes.

Before a thorough discussion of the intertidal zone can be appreciated,
it is necessary to have at least a passing knowledge of some of the characteristics of both the physical and biological aspects of the coast.

The Physical Conditions of a Rocky Shore

Since we are restricted to a description of only one geographic area of
the coast, the moderately exposed rocky shore of the Moss Beach, California area has been selected as it furnishes the greatest diversity of niches,
plants, and animals. The physical stresses which are generated by the
rhythmic tidal exposure, the changing climate, and the different areas of
wave shock all combine to produce special adaptations in the form, func-
tioning, and behavior of the plants and animals inhabiting the littoral (tidal)
zones.

The ecological niche is a convenient concept to use in noting the occurrence
of a species, and its "way of life." The term (niche) is used to refer to a
complete set of environmental conditions, both physical and biotic, and the
manner in which a particular animal or plant is adapted to it. The ecological
definition is "way of life." The complete definition of a niche is difficult,
but we can pick out some of the obvious features of each niche. The living
organism which is usually found in some spot (habitat) must be adapted to
survive under the most unfavorable extremes of conditions that occur in its
environment. The sum total of all of these factors is the niche.

Most niche concepts are based primarily on food because all organisms
must live where food is available to them. Intertidal sea weeds (algae) produce their own food from light and materials in the ocean itself and are food
for intertidal animals of many types. Some animals eat only other animals,
some eat everything edible and are scavengers, like the hermit crabs.
Barnacles and mussels filter planktonic food out of the sea water and are
modified for that function and also are located where the waves will bring
them food. Tide pool fish and crabs feed upon organic debris that accumulates in the shallow depressions.

Intertidal plants are generally found where they can be assured of an ade-
quate supply of food-like materials such as carbon dioxide, chemical nutrients and sunlight. They are also found where they can find a place for
their holdfast or anchor, such as on a rock or shell of some animal.

Physical factors of the environment are important in determining the
limits of distribution of an organism in the field. Some of the factors that
can be noted in the field are listed below.

Wave action, changing tides, and rain all help to remove waste materials produced by the animals of the intertidal areas. Some of the wastes are used and assimilated by other animals or plants as necessary nutrients or fertilizers. For example, CO_2 and animal nitrates are used by plants in their photosynthesis. Plant by-products, like oxygen and sugars, are used by animals as foods, or as necessary chemicals for metabolism.

There is a great competition among the seashore organisms for space in which to live. Those best adapted for survival will have the greatest advantages in securing this living space. Some animals like the worms, sea urchins, and boring clams make their own living space by boring holes in rock, mud, or wood. Sometimes animals and some algae live on top of other animals or plants. Some red algae can be found on almost all other things at the beach. Limpets and barnacles can be found on other molluscs or arthropods. Still other animals are parasitic or live as commensals with other animals. Crabs, scale worms, and round and flat worms live in the mantle cavity of chitons and other molluscs. Many flat worms and flat-topped crabs are well adapted to live under rocks. Many animals live only on certain types of sea weeds like the Limpet (*Acmea incessa*) which is found only on the Feather Boa Kelp (*Egregia menziesii*).

The temperature of the environment for most organisms is perhaps of the utmost importance, for it is the temperature that regulates the "rate of living" of all organisms (the enzyme effect). Enzymes are the organic catalysts that control the rate of biochemical reactions within an organism. They, in effect, control the "rate of living" which, in turn, controls the behavior of the organism. Most organisms have a very limited range of temperature tolerance. When exposed to temperatures below minimal the enzymes are relatively inactive, and when temperatures exceed the maximum the enzymes are destroyed.

The type of substrate along the San Mateo coast is extremely variable even within short distances. Some of the types found are the rocky cliffs, ledges, boulder, and cobble areas near the cliffs. Further away from the base of the steep abutment we can find sand, mud, clay or mixtures of these on solid rock reefs. Piers or breakwaters like the ones at Princeton, California, offer man-made substrates. The type and permanence of the substrate are important factors in limiting the distribution of plants and animals.

Sand serves as a good substrate for the Sand Dollars (*Dendraster excentricus*), Serpent Stars (*Ophioplocus sp.*), Sand Crabs (*Emerita analoga*), and various fishes, such as the Flounder, Sand Dabs, and Sting Rays. However, this loose, shifting benthos is a poor place for the attachment of algae holdfasts, California mussel byssal fibers, or barnacles. Rocky or other firm substrates serve the other set of organisms.

The wave-shock factor is of importance where wave impact is great. Animals must have some structural and/or behavioral adaptations to maintain their presence in any such area. These adaptations are noted in a hydrodynamic body shape which lets water flow easily over them, in a sucker-like foot or firm holdfast as seen in oysters, mussels, and chitons or in some flattened body shape which lets them hide in cracks in the rock when the waves are breaking. Plants also have mechanisms that allow them to adapt to wave action. Some of these are: root-like structures called holdfasts, rubbery bodies to bend with the flow of the waves or solid encrusting bodies to hug the rocks.

Tides, Their Causes and Controls

The most important factor of the intertidal area is the movements of the water called the tides. The tides are caused by the gravitational pull of bodies in space upon the earth and the waters of the earth and the rotation of the earth. The main bodies that affect and regulate the tides are the sun and moon. The moon is smaller than the sun, but much closer to the earth and it, therefore, exerts a greater pull. Distortion of the water surface of the earth by this attraction causes the water to bulge or pile up on the sides of the earth toward and away from the moon. (See diagram #1 and #2.) These bulges are the areas of high tides and the depressions between the bulges are the low tides.

The sun has a similar but smaller effect. (See diagram #4.) When the gravitational pull of the sun opposes that of the moon, the pull of the sun is obscured. These tides are called Neap tides during which the high tides are lower while the low tides are higher than if the moon and sun were lined up because of the opposing attractions. When both sun and moon are lined up, their pulls work together and the tides are called Spring tides. The Spring tides occur every 14 days and the high tides are higher while the low tides are lower than those recorded during Neap tides.

There are two high and two low tides at any one place on the coast during a 24 hour and 52 minute period due to the rotation of the earth under the water bulges. (See diagram #3.) Each high and low tide is 6 hours and 13 minutes apart while successive high or low tides are 12 hours and 26 minutes apart. The complete tidal cycle starts about one hour later each day because the moon circles the earth on a lunar or 28 day month while we go by a calendar or 30-31 day month.

The Tides

I.   Earth's Movements (South polar Projections)
    A.   Individual motions
        (1)   revolve around sun (lin. 365+ days
        (2)   rotate on axes (24 hrs.)
        (3)   revolve around common center
            with moon (as moon revolves around
            earth.) (28 days)

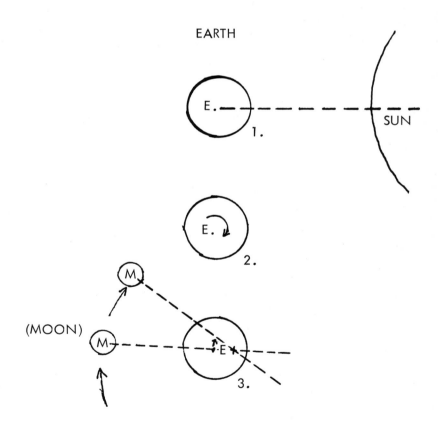

B. Total Movement

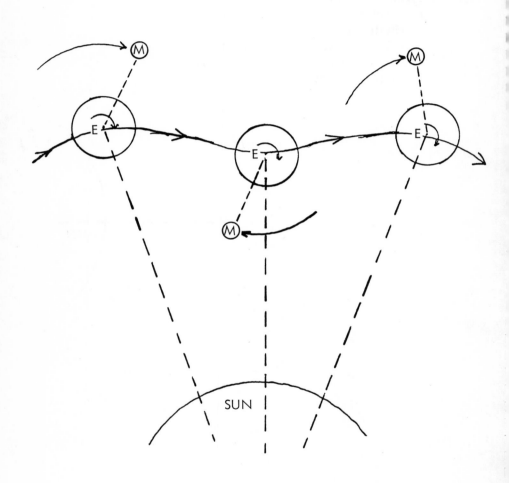

II. The water reacts to forces
   A.   Gravity of moon

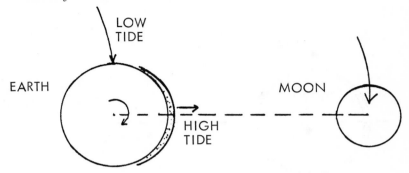

   B.   Inertia of earth-moon interaction
       (movement #3)

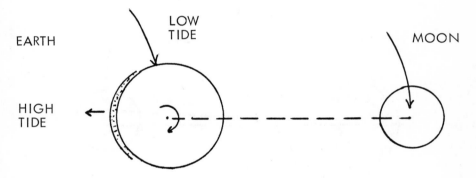

   C.   Composite forces/reactions

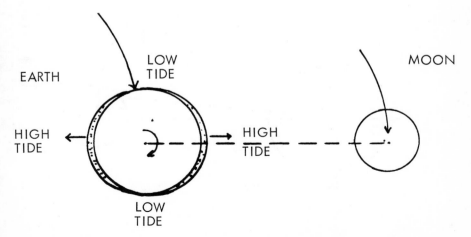

III.   Water and Earth movements and time

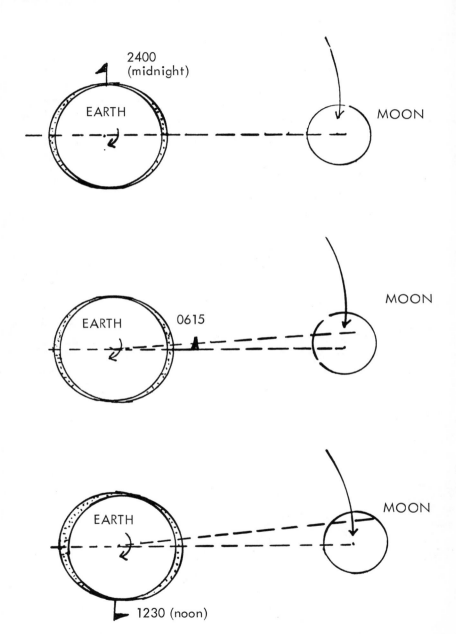

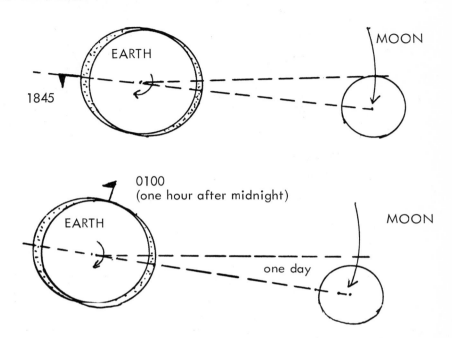

IV. Moon gravity and moon/earth inertia (x) 240,000 miles distance
interacting with
Sun gravity sun/earth inertia (y) 93,000,000 miles distance

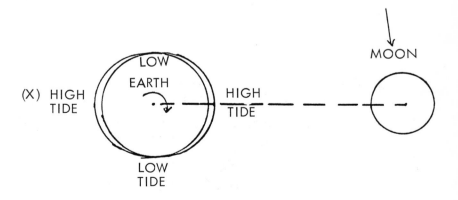

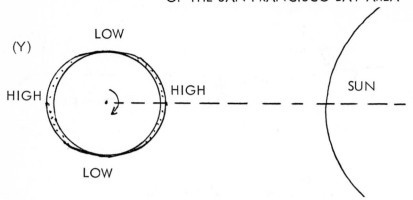

B. Composite
    Tide (x) – Tide (y)

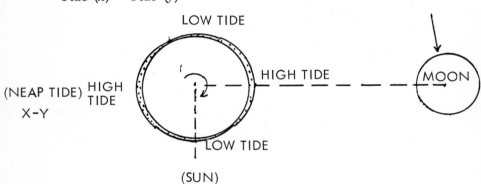

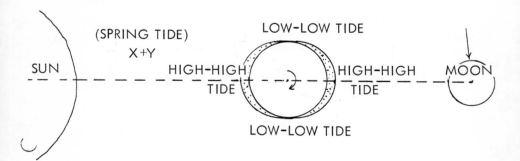

Degree of Tidal Exposure

Tidal exposure is the time that organisms are not covered by water (low tide). This factor leads to conditions that directly affect plants and animals, and these living things must adapt to the change in conditions in order to survive. Some of the more important conditions with which they must cope follow.

Desiccation (drying out) is a very serious problem for organisms that are marine or aquatic. Their internal chemistry is adapted for a watery medium and if exposed to air on warm sunny days, they will lose water by evaporation. Some animals can crawl under rocks or sea weeds and are thus protected from direct sun rays. Other nonmoving animals and plants must have some adaption to protect themselves. Sea anemones, sea urchins, and some other sessile animals cover their bodies with sand, algae, gravel, or shells. Many have tough or slimy skins which prevent water loss and/or large stores of internal water. This internal water helps them remain moist, and maintain a lower body temperature through evaporation.

Temperature variation is a very important and critical factor for exposed animals. (See enzyme effect.) In direct sun and attached to the exposed rock, the body temperature of a mussel or barnacle may reach 100° F on many occasions. Even in small contained tide pools the temperature may reach 80° F. During the winter the exposed animal may be subjected to below freezing temperatures. The variation of sea water itself has a small range of temperature, usually from 52° F to about 56° F along this coast. Marine animals can usually withstand temperatures down to about 30° F because of the large content of salts in their bodies, and conversely they are cooled during hot spells by evaporation of body water. Temperature, however, is still a very important factor in limiting their distribution.

Salinity varies according to the amount of evaporation or rainfall in any given area. Intertidal plants and animals must be able to tolerate, avoid, or regulate against the increased or decreased amounts of salt in their immediate surroundings. These factors are especially important to those organisms living in small isolated tide pools.

Oxygen availability sometimes becomes a factor. If animals are crowded into a small tide pool during low tides they may utilize oxygen faster than it dissolves into their surrounding water. Most gas exchange takes place across moist membranes. If animals become dry due to exposure they probably also suffer from lack of oxygen. Burrowing animals also suffer from reduced oxygen during low tides.

Tidal Zones

The tidal zones are characterized by the degrees of tidal exposure and the characteristic groups of plants and animals common to each. The species used to describe a certain zone are not restricted to that zone only. The overlapping of one zone with another will become obvious as you collect and look for plants and animals at Moss Beach. It must be remembered that distinct zones as such do not exist. The degree of tidal exposure is continuous, but as a convenience, the intertidal area has been divided into four zones.

The zones can be defined by tidal level on vertical surfaces only. The extent of individual zones is a complexity of the shoreline, the surf, and the surrounding conditions. The change in these conditions widens or narrows each zone, and also widens or narrows the range of distribution for organisms. Thus the extent and absolute height of a zone is variable but the defining plant and animal groups maintain their relative positions. The table given below illustrates the vertical zonation of plants and animals from Moss Beach. The numbers refer to tidal heights above and below sea level under calm and sheltered conditions.

Sand Crab

CHARACTERISTIC ROCKY SHORE PLANTS AND ANIMALS
Table No. 1 from Moss Beach, California

Animals	Plants	Zones
I Periwinkles, Pill Bugs, Limpets, Acorn Barnacles Gray Barnacles	*Prasiola sp.*	Highest high tides +6.7' Exposed except at hi-hi spring tides 2-3 hrs. twice a month mean of high tides +5.0'
II Limpets, Black Turban Snail Periwinkles Barnacles Lined Shore Crab Purple Shore Crab California Chiton Mossy Chiton	Rock Weeds Sea Lettuce Goat's Beard Sea Tar	Covered only during high tide 2-3 hrs. twice a day neap tide mean of higher lows +2.5'
III Abalone Kelp Crab Starfish Chitons Sea Anemones Volcano Limpet Brown Turban	Rock Weed Feather Boa Kelp Red Coralline algae red and brown algae predominate	Exposed only during low tides 2-3 hrs. twice a day neap tide mean of lower low 0.0'
IV Purple Sea Urchin Cancer Crabs Red Abalone Nudibranchs Solitary Corals Octopus California Mussel Goose-neck Barnacle	Mainly red and brown algae Coralline algae the large kelps the sea palms Surf Grass	Exposed only at Low-Low tides Exposed 2-3 hrs. twice a month spring tide lowest low tide -1.6'

Moss Beach, California. Hinterland and
Tidal Flats.

In a trip from the car to the water's edge (beach) you can see a tremen-
dous variety of plants and animals. Some of these are found only on the
coastal strip (hinterland) because of weather conditions, salt in the air,
or soil types. The following plants are the most common and most obvious
on this and similar locations.

Monterey Pine

The Monterey Pine (*Pinus radiata*)
is the fastest growing of the pines and
reaches a height of more than 75 feet.
These trees line the roads approach-
ing Moss Beach and grow wild along
much of the coast. The dark green
needles are found growing in clumps
of three per bunch and each needle is
about five inches long. The female
cones, which are attached to branches
and trunk, are more than five inches
long and contain many edible seeds.
Birds, squirrels, and other animals
eat these seeds. The male cones are
small and found at the ends of the
branches.

The Monterey Cypress (*Cupressus macrocarpa*) is a tall, beautiful cone tree. It also grows along the roads and coast. Many of these trees have been planted as windbreaks, but some also are found as a natural plant. They have small (1-1 1/2 inch), roundish cones which open when dry and produce small, sharp-edged brown seeds. The leaves are small, dark green overlapping scales. This tree has the smallest natural range of any native western plant. It normally grows only on a few exposed points in the Carmel and Monterey area.

Monterey Pine Needles

Two lupines are common to the coastal strand. The first is the Blue Beach Lupine (*Lupinus chamissonis*). It is a low, shrubby plant with blue flowers and greenish leaves. Each leaf has several blades all spreading out from a single petiole or stalk. (See glossary under "Palmate" Compound leaves).

The second lupine, the Tree Lupine (*Lupinus arboreus*), has bright yellow flowers and is a bush about four feet tall. In both of these lupines the flowers change in the fall to a bean-like pod which rattles when dry. The seeds are dark brown and furnish food for rodents and birds.

The Coastal Salt Bush (*Atriplex leucophylla*) is a small, low-growing bush with horizontal branches. The entire plant seldom exceeds 8 inches in height. It has small yellow flowers and distinctive red, fleshy, berry-like bracts.

California Blackberries (*Rubus vitifolius*) occur in patches where they cover the ground with a spreading nature growing over other plants. The leaves are pinnately compound with

Cone

Scales

Monterey Cypress

3-5 leaflets. Each leaflet has serrated margins and thorns on the petiole. The white one inch flowers form
nice, edible, black berries which provide food for birds, small mammals,
and man! Be careful when walking
through these patches because the
branches are covered with many large
thorns.

New Zealand Spinach (*Tetragonia
expansa*) is a low, prostrate succulent growing over the hills at Moss
Beach and is another edible plant. The
leaves are greenish, arrowhead-shaped
and thick. The flowers are small and
form a nut-like pod hooked to the stem
where the leaves attach.

Sweet Alyssum (*Alyssum maritimum*) is a sweet-smelling flower and
is an escapee of the garden. The plants
are about five inches tall with lance-
shaped leaves and pretty, small white
flowers arranged in a bouquet on the
ends of the main stems. These flowers
form small dark seeds which readily
fall from the flower (salique). The
remaining dry portion is called the
"Devil's Eyeglass" because of its round,
transparent nature.

Blue Beach Lupine

California Blackberries

Tree Lupine

Weeds of the genera *Brassica spp.*, *Capsella spp.*, are found all throughout the coastal strand. The group includes the wild mustards; the yellow, white and black varieties, the wild turnips, flax, cress, and the Shepherd's Purse, etc. These plants generally have lobed, green leaves and the plants are from one to six feet tall. The leaves and roots of many of the mustards are generally edible. (See the chapter on the Grasslands.)

German Ivy (*Senecio mikanioides*) is a long, low-creeping vine with dark, shiny, green leaves growing as a ground cover along the coast. The single flowers are yellow. This flower is found in many other biomes in the Bay Area.

Sweet Alyssum

Mustard – General

New Zealand Spinach

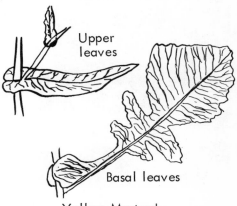

Upper leaves

Basal leaves

Yellow Mustard

Another colorful plant is the Hottentot Fig (*Mesembryanthemum edule*),
a low, succulent herb with three-sided,
thick, curved leaves. This is the plant
used by the highway department as a
dirt binder along road cuts and fills.
This plant has gone wild and is found
in many places along the coast. It has
reddish (2-3 inches in length) leaves and
red, purple, yellow, or white flowers.
The flowers have many petals.

M. chilense, the Sea Fig, is similar
to the Hottentot Fig, but is smaller
(about half as big), both in leaf size and
flower size. The flowers also tend to
be magenta.

M. floribundum, another ice plant
common along our coast has small (1/2
inch), cylindrical, succulent, green
leaves. These leaves are arranged
in an opposite manner and the leaves
and flowers grow out from a woody,
dry stem. The flower is small (3/4
inch diameter) and may vary from purple to lavender to white.

German Ivy

Hottentot Fig

Sea Fig

Small Ice Plant

In continuing the walk toward the beach you will note many wild flowers, grasses, weeds, shrubs, vines, and ferns. For a better description or key to these plants see other parts of this book or note the reference materials.

Leaving the hinterland behind, it will usually be necessary to climb down a rather steep embankment. The "cliff" is formed by the wave action on the land, and marks the border between "land and the intertidal areas. " Extreme care should be exercised while making this descent. The sand portion at the bottom of this cliff leads to the water's edge and is called "Zone I" of the intertidal area.

The Open Coast at Moss Beach, California.
Mr. Monroe in Zone I.

Zone I Plants and Animals

When standing on the dry beach you are in Zone I. The following plants and animals can be seen by looking on exposed rocks, under rocks, in the sand, or on the beach. Be sure to replace the rocks in their original position.

Zone I is the uppermost rocky beach, wetted in its upper parts by spray only and in its lower parts by high tides only. This area is bare rock and sand generally, but in many cases there are sparce areas of green, threaded-like algae called *Prasiola*.

The animals discussed below eat other animals, microscopic algae, detritus, or sea weeds. Many sea weeds are broken from their holdfasts and are washed by surf into this area. Almost any algae can be found here after storms and these algae provide food for other Zone I animals.

While walking on the beach (Zone I) or while down on the tidal flats you will note a variety of birds. The following are some of the most common and obvious animals of the rocky coast. Some of the birds are migratory, but many are permanent residents of this area. Many of these shore birds will also be found on sandy beaches, mud flats, in Bay marshes, and on the freshwater lakes in the area.

Usually, the most obvious birds seen along this coast are the beautiful sea gulls. There are more than 10 species of gulls found on the peninsula. The gulls are good swimming or we should say good floating birds and have a poetic and majestic flight pattern. They can be seen wheeling, swooping, hovering in flight or wading along the shore. They ride up-currents of air along the cliff edges for long periods of time without flapping their wings. All gulls are fish eaters and/or scavengers. Before storms they will fly inland to freshwater lakes or protected parking lots or roofs. These gulls nest at Pt. Lobos near Carmel, California, and on other protected points and islands along the coast and in other western lakes. Most young birds are mottled brown for the first few years and then they acquire the adult color pattern.

Ring-billed Gull

The California Gull (*Larus californicus*) is a gull of medium size (about 22 inches long) with light gray back feathers and is white under the wings and along the lower body. There is a red spot on the lower bill and the feet have a greenish color. The red spot on the bill is a help in feeding the young birds. The newly-hatched gull will peck at the red spot and when this happens the parent bird will give food to the fledgling.

Ring-billed Gulls (*Larus delawarensis*) are smaller than the California Gull and there is a dark ring completely around the bill. The legs of these birds are yellowish. This is the most common small gull inland from the coast. One prominent feature in the young bird is a black band on its tail.

Adult Western Gulls (*Larus occi-dentalis*) are about 20-24 inches long. They have a dark feather pattern on the back and upper wings (the mantle), but all the rest of the body is pure white. These gulls have pink legs and a red spot on the lower bill.

The Herring Gull (*Larus argentatus*) is a migratory bird that has a pearly gray mantle with black wing tips and pinkish legs. The Herring Gull, like most other gulls, is pure white under the wings and on the body. This gull also has a whitish eye.

Herring Gull

Killdeer (*Charadrius vociferus*) are small (robin-sized), active birds that can be seen running rapidly along the shore or following the waves back and forth. They have thin legs, gray back feathers and two black bands on their white breasts. The Killdeer has a char-acteristic call which sounds like its name and it also gives a "dee-dee-dee" call. Their main food at the beach is small crustaceans, worms, and dead animal materials. Killdeer are also found in dry, desert areas, and stream beds eating insects and other small animals.

Killdeer

There are six species of sandpipers along this coast. These small (7-9 inch), grayish birds with delicate legs run along the beach eating any small animals, like worms and crabs. The most common bird of this type is the Spotted Sandpiper (*Actitis macularia*) and it can be recognized by the large spots on the breast during the spring and summer. It is white underneath during other seasons and grayish on its back.

Spotted Sandpiper

The gulls, killdeer, and sandpipers
are some of the most common birds
along the coast, but not the only ones
to be seen. Many "land" type birds
may occasionally come down to the
shore. For descriptions of the "other"
birds see the reference materials.

Great Beach Hopper

Zone I +6.7' to +5.0'

One of the first invertebrate animals
encountered in Zone I is the Great
Beach Hopper (*Orchestoidea californiana*). These nocturnal beach hop-
pers or sand fleas are ivory-colored
amphipods (compressed side to side).
They grow from 1 inch to 2 1/2 inches
long, and are usually found in great
numbers in piles of rotting sea weed
or in small holes in the sand. These
eat the algae and provide food for many
birds and other animals.

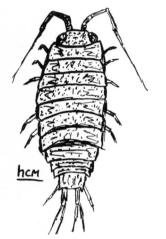

Pill Bug

The Pill Bug (*Ligia occidentalis*) is
almost terrestrial and can be found in
the dry areas almost always above the
high tide marks. *Ligia* is blackish,
segmented, very active, and usually
found under rocks. These Pill Bugs
grow to 1 1/2 inches and are isopods
(compressed top to bottom). This animal is a scavenger eating any organic
debris available. *Ligia* serve as a
source of food for many birds.

The Periwinkles (*Littorina planaxis*)
are small, dirty-gray snails found clustered in crevices of exposed rocks.
The tip of the shell is blunt and a polished area is found near the aperture.
These 1/4 inch snails have an operculum which can be seen covering the
opening into the shell. Periwinkles

Periwinkle

eat diatoms and small bits of plant material, with a rasp-like tongue called
a radula.

Acmea digitalis and *Acmea scabra*
are limpets that are very common at
Moss Beach. They live on exposed
rock faces with the Periwinkles and
Acorn Barnacles. Both species are
about 1 inch long, and are herbivores,
scraping algae from the rocks with
their radulas. *Acmea digitalis* (the
Common Rock Limpet) has the apex of
the shell displaced to one end. *Acmea
scabra* (the Ribbed Limpet) is flatter
and has more conspicuous ribbing.
Both have dark markings but *Acmea
digitalis* has darker and more obvious
markings inside the shell. There are
about 17 species of limpets found at
Moss Beach and a reference book should
be consulted for more complete descriptions.

The Acorn Barnacles (*Balanus glandula*) are whitish, sessile crustaceans
about 1/2 inch in diameter. They are
very abundant on exposed rocks. Note
the door-like features of the shell. The
barnacles are all filter feeders and can
not feed unless they are covered by
spray or running water. When this happens they will open their doors and
rake the water with their jointed feet
that are covered with hair-like projections. The Brown Barnacle (*Chthamalus
dalli*) is found in the same area as the
Acorn Barnacle, but it is smaller and
flatter. When climbing over the rocks
be careful because these shells can cut
the hands.

In small, permanent, spray pools in
Zone I you may find most of the above
mentioned animals plus a small red

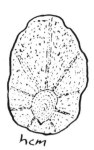

Common Rock Limpet

Ribbed Limpet

Acorn Barnacle

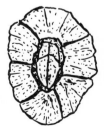

Brown Barnacle

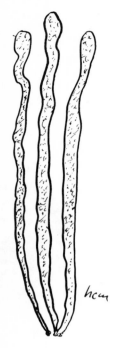

Enteromorpha

copepod called *Tigriopus californicus* and a yellowish-green algae (*Enteromorpha intestinalis*).

The Red Copepod (a crustacean) is a scavenger and is able to adjust to great changes in salinity and temperature. These copepods eat detritus, such as dead snails, or any other dead animal material that accumulates in their pools. The entire life cycle is maintained in these warm, salty areas. This copepod will not normally be found in lower tide pools where much wave action occurs.

Enteromorpha is predominant in the pools that are subject to more fresh water than normal. Although it can grow in lower (more marine) pools it is in greatest abundance closer to the cliffs where fresh water drains down to the ocean.

Zone II + 5.0' to + 2.5'

Tide Pool   Lower Zone II
Upper Zone III

As you continue walking out from the shore you will soon be in Zone II. This is a high tide region with more or less permanent tide pools. At Moss Beach, Zone II is very close to the base of the cliffs and can be distinguished by the following common and obvious types of algae.

You will find two types of Rock Weeds attached to exposed rocks. These are *Fucus* and *Pelvetiopsis*. Both are dichotomous, branching, flattened, brown algae (Phaeophyta) that look dark brownish-green. *Fucus* is the larger of the two types. These plants have root-like holdfasts that help them stay on the rocks. The swollen tips of the branch-like thallus contain the reproductive conceptacles. Another brown algae that looks like tar on the rocks is called *Ralfsia*. This plant is only a few cell layers thick.

Two types of red algae (Rhodophyta) common in Zone II are the Goat's Beard (*Endocladia muricata*) and a Red Rock Weed called *Gigartina cristata*. This Gigartina has small papillae-like outgrowths on the surface of the plant and the entire plant is about 4-6 inches long and about 1/2 inch wide. *Gigartina cristata* appears blackish-red and is rubbery with a lobed or split leaf-like thallus. Goat's Beard is small, thin, and wiry. It is a red algae, but looks brownish. This plant is mossy in appearance and grows to about 2-3 inches in length.

The last type of algae mentioned here is the green algae (Chlorophyta) of which there are two obvious members in Zone II. These are *Ulva spp.* (Sea

Rock Weed
(*Fucus furcatus*)

Rock Weed
(*Pelvetiopsis limitata*)

Lettuce) and a bright green, tufted algae, *Cladophora trichotoma* (Mermaid's Pin Cushion). Both of these green algae, along with all the reds and browns, provide food for the herbivores in Zone II.

A microscopic group of algae called the sea scums or blue-green algae (Cyanophyta), and the diatoms (Chrysophyta), provide food for the smaller marine plant eaters such as some copepods. For identification purposes use some of the reference books mentioned in the bibliography. Algae are extremely hard to identify or key out, so we wish you good luck.

Leaving the plants and returning to the animals you will note the following Zone II animals in, on, or under the exposed rocks or in the protected areas.

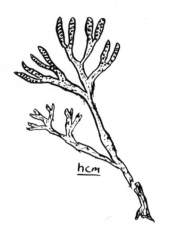

Rock Weed
(*Pelvetia spp.*)

Goat's Beard

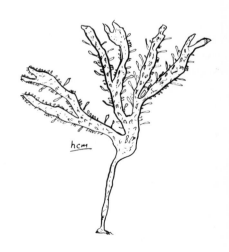

Red Rock Weed
(*Gigartina cristata*)

The Zone II Periwinkle (*Littorina scutulata*) has a checkered pattern and a pointed tip on the shell. The shell lacks the polished area near the opening noted in *Littorina planaxis* but is about the same size (1/4 to 1/2 inch).

Both of the Limpets (*Acmeas*) mentioned for Zone I are also found in this area. The only other really common mollusks found in Zone II are two carnivorous snails; the Unicorn Snail and the Rock Snail, and one very common herbivorous gastropod, the Black Turban Snail. Carnivorous snails have an oblong opening into the shell, while herbivores have a rounded opening.

The Unicorn (*Acanthina spirata*) can be noted by its tooth near the opening of the shell, its patterns of faint, short lines, and its blunt spindle shape. The Unicorn eats barnacles, mussels, and other snails of this zone. The food is obtained through a hole drilled in the shell by the radula. These snails can be found in cracks of the larger rocks.

The Rock Snail (*Thais emarginata*) looks much like the Unicorn but lacks the tooth. Rock Snails have spiral, brownish lines on a greenish-gray shell. These snails use their radulas to bore holes in the shells of mussels, clams, limpets, and barnacles. Rock Snails are about 3/4 inch long, have a blunter shell and a wider operculum opening than the Unicorns. These are found in groups intermixed with the *Acanthina*.

The Black Turban Snail (*Tegula funebralis*) is the most common gastropod in both Zone II and III. It is about 1 inch tall, is squat, and has a black outer color. This color may be worn

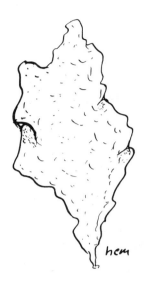

Ulva

Periwinkle

The Unicorn Snail

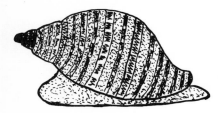

Purple Rock Snail

Black Turban Snail

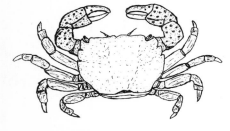

Purple Shore Crab

off the apex of the shell where a dull white color shows through. These animals will be found in dense clusters in grooves in the rock or under rocks. Turban Snails eat algae, and possess a feeding device or radula which is rasp-like in structure. Turban Snails, like most other snails have a protein flap called an operculum that they pull shut after them when they withdraw into their shells.

Other common animals in Zone II are the crabs and their relatives. Most crabs in this area are scavengers and will eat anything, dead or alive. They will be found under the rocks in great numbers and in mixtures of various types. Male crabs can usually be distinguished from females by the tail flexed under their thorax. The tail of most males is pointed while the tail of the female is rounded and, during the winter, heavy with eggs (in berry).

One of the characteristic crabs of Zone II is the Purple Shore Crab (*Hemigrapsus nudus*) which is a decapod (ten walking legs) crustacean. This scavenger has purple spots on its reddish pinchers which can give a sharp pinch. Like most crabs, shore crabs scurry sideways in their search for food. These crabs are about 2-4 inches across the rather square carapace (shell). The males turn redder during the winter breeding season. Like most crabs they can cast off their legs (autotomy) whenever they are threatened. This is a protective device that allows them freedom when an appendage is pinned down by a rock, boulder, or predator. These crabs can be found in association with many other crabs under the rocks. The other crabs in the same area are the Lined Shore Crab, the Porcelain Crabs, and the Hermit Crabs.

The Lined Shore Crab (*Pachygrapsus crassipes*) is greenish-red with purple stripes, and has large, red claws. This very active crab is about the same size as the Purple Shore Crab and is very difficult to capture if not surprised. They scurry among the rocks searching for food and will eat small worms, detritus, and other appropriate food.

Two flattened crabs, the Porcelain Crab (*Petrolisthes cinctipes*) and the Flat Crab (*Pachycheles rudis*), live under the rocks, scurrying into deep cracks when exposed. The Porcelain Crab is the larger of the two (about 1 1/2 inches across) and is very flat with its flattened pinchers held in front of the body. A smaller, less active crab with heavier but smaller claws living deeper in crevices and under the rocks is the Flat Crab. Both tend to lose legs readily. Most of these crabs are very active at night when they search for food, mates, and when they are not in danger of drying out.

The Common Hermit Crab (*Pagurus samuelis*) and the Hairy Hermit Crab (*Pagurus hirsutiusculus*) are little Anomuran crabs (four pairs of walking legs including the pinchers) and are the clowns of the beach. They are also the garbage collectors cleaning all the shells of other animals and eating parts of sea weeds and dead animals. They are constantly running around looking for food or empty shells for a new home. Both of these crabs are olive drab in color, but the Common Hermit Crab

Lined Shore Crab

Porcelain Crab

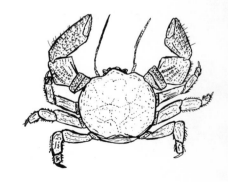

Flat Crab

Hermit Crab

has red antennae with blue or white
bands on the legs.   The Hairy Hermit
Crab has the appendages the same color
as the rest of the body.   They are generally found in *Tegula* shells, or, if
near sandy beaches, in Purple Olive
shells (*Olivella biplicata*).

Other animals found under the rocks
to any extent are Brittle Stars, Flat
Worms, Gill Worms, and Serpulid
Worms, and small amphipod crustaceans.

All three of the Brittle Stars common
to this area, (*Ophioplocus esmarki*),
(*Ophiothrix spiculata*), (*Amphiodia occidentalis*), are from 1/2 to 2 inches in
total diameter.   All Brittle Stars usually have five arms, or rays, and all
are found living on the undersurface of
rocks in the sand.   The first has a
granular, central disc, and is brownish-
white while the second has short spines
on each ray and may be bright orange
in color.   The third has the narrowest
rays, and may have black and white
banding on the rays.   All are detritus
(ooze) eaters, and generally turn redder

Purple Olive Shell

during the breeding season. Sift through
the sand with your fingers and you will
turn up many of these animals. When
handling these animals be careful because their "arms" fall off readily as
their name implies.

Two common flatworms (*Notoplana
acticola* and *Alloioplana californica*)
are found under and on the rocks turned
over in Zone II. These one inch long
worms are gray or greenish, harmless,
and can be put on your thumbnail for
better examination. Both have a many
branched gut and eat microscopic organisms and any decaying meat. These
worms, in turn, serve as food for small
fish and crabs.

The Hairy-gilled Worms (*Cirriformia
luxuriosa*) live in burrows in the mud,
or in sand in tide pools, or under rocks.
Their gills extend to the surface of the
sand, and look like groups of waving
hair. The adult worm is about 4 inches
long. These worms are ciliary feeders
and eat very small particulate plants
and animals.

Flatworm
(*Notoplana acticola*)

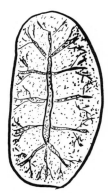

Flatworm
(*Alloioplana californica*)

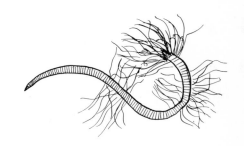

Hairy-gilled Worms

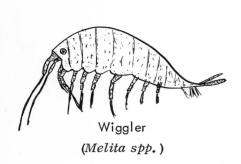

Wiggler
(*Melita spp.*)

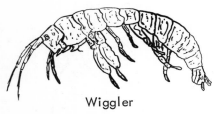

Wiggler
(*Elasmopus spp.*)

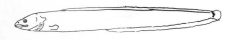

Black Prickleback

Rockweed Gunnel

Circle Serpulids (*Spirorbis spp.*) are tiny 1/4 inch worms with calcium tubes that appear as small, white coils or circles on the surface of rocks. Note that some coil to the right and some coil to the left. The tube is about 0.1 inch in diameter. These small animals filter the water drawn into their tubes for food.

The Wigglers (*Melita palmata* and *Elasmopus rapax*) are small, 1/4 inch amphipods compressed laterally (side to side). They wiggle about on the undersurface of the rocks, and among the holdfasts on the algae and mussels. Note that they seem to swim on their sides. Place a small bunch of algae in a white pan and you will see many of these wigglers swimming about. Wigglers eat diatoms and other minute plankton.

In most of the permanent tide pools in Zones II, III, and IV we find certain marine fishes and marine algae. The most common ones are described below.

Black Prickleback (*Epigeichthys atro-purpureus*) and the Rockweed Gunnel (*Xererpes fucorum*) are often but erroneously called "blennies." True blennies, such as the Rock Pool Blenny (*Hypsoblennies gilberti*), are shorter and thicker than Pricklebacks and Gunnels, and somewhat resemble Sculpins (see below). The Gunnels and Pricklebacks are eel-like fish that usually are between 3 and 6 inches long, but both may exceed a foot in length. Their coloration is variable due to the variety of food eaten. They are generally reddish-brown but may be bright green, gray, or white. These fish eat algae and small invertebrates.

They are often caught under rocks, in
tide pools, and are reputed to be good
to eat.

Sculpins *(Clinocottus spp.)*, *(Oligocottus spp.)* have large heads, are from
1 to 6 inches long, and have eyes on the
top of their heads. They also have
"eyebrows" that look like pitchforks.
Their colors are variable giving them
good concealment. Their stiff pelvic
fins allow them to cling to the rocks
during wave action. These animals
eat worms, small crustaceans, and
some algae.

The Clingfish *(Sicyogaster maean-
drica)* sucks onto rocks using modified pelvic fins. They have a large
head and a short, tapering body. They
are usually less than 3 inches long.

The primary tide pool plants are
the red algae and are usually hard,
calcified, or encrusting algae such as
Corallina, Bossea, and *Lithothamnion.* Other branching, non-encrusting
red algae in these pools are *Grateloupia* and *Prionotis.* None of these
plants have good common names. Note
the drawings for visual descriptions.

Only two intertidal flowering plants
are found in Zones II, III, IV. One is
called Eel Grass *(Zostera marina).*
This plant is dark green and up to 4 feet
long. Its leaves are about 8 mm.
wide. Eel Grass has a white, beady
flower. The other flowering plant is
Surf Grass with two species: *Phyllospadix torreyi* and *P. scouleri.*
Both are thinner than Eel Grass, usually less than 4 mm. wide. These
plants provide protection for fishes,
snails, and the octopus. All three
plants grow in sandy areas where their

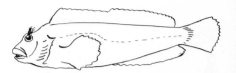

Rock Pool Blenny

Shiner Perch

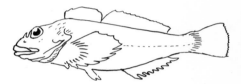

Sculpin

Clingfish

Bossea spp.

68

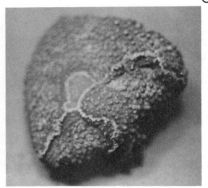

Lithothamnion sp.

roots allow them to maintain position. Within these roots you may find more than 30 species of Annelids, Molluscs, and other invertebrates.

Many animals live on top of the rocks in this zone that are not found on the sides or underneath those rocks.

The California Mussels (*Mytilus californianus*) are found on top of the rocks lower in Zone II and in the two lower zones where the surf is high. Mussels are found in great masses attached to the rocks by byssal fibers that are thread-like, protein secretions. These bivalves are bluish-black and grow up to 5 inches long. They filter microscopic plants and animals (plankton) out of sea water using their gills as a strainer. Due to this food-acquiring habit, these mussels may be poisonous during the spring months. These mussels, like other sessile animals, spawn (liberate eggs and sperms)

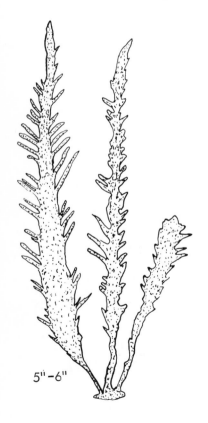

5"-6"

Grateloupia sp.

16"-24"

Prionotis sp.

into the sea water where fertilization takes place. The free-living larvae feed in the open sea, grow, and return to the intertidal area where they settle in clumps forming new mussel beds.

There are three common chitons, or sea cradles, in Zone II. One is the Mossy Chiton (*Mopalia muscosa*) which is 3 inches long, oval in shape, and has a fuzzy, outer edge (girdle) around the 8 overlapping shells. This chiton can be found in depressions in the rocks. Another chiton can be found under the rocks and is called the Butterfly Chiton (*Ischnochiton regularis*). It is pinkish on the inside of the shell, and from mottled orange to greenish-blue on the outside. The third chitons (*Lepidozona spp.*) have no good common name and are less than 2 inches long with angular, reddish, mottled plates. There are about 15 species of chitons found at Moss Beach and they all have 8 overlapping shells. They are very hard to identify. All chitons are herbivores and graze using the radula to scrape up small plant materials. Animals and sand are accidental food materials.

hcm

Mossy Chiton

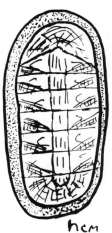

hcm

Butterfly Chiton

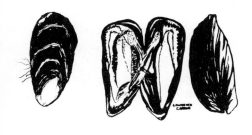

California Mussels

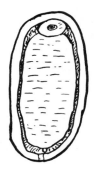

Lepidozona spp.

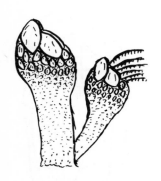

Red Barnacle

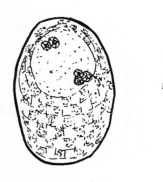

Goose-necked Barnacle

The Red Barnacle (*Tetraclita squamosa*) grows to about 1 inch or twice the size of the Acorn Barnacle. It is dull red, and looks like a volcano. These red barnacles are not found in masses, but are solitary. We also find the Goose-neck Barnacles (*Pollicipes polymerus*) clustered on the surf-swept rocks. They are whitish, and have a black, fleshy stalk. These, like all barnacles, are filter feeders, feeding only when the surf is covering them, or when the tide is in. All barnacles are crustaceans, and like the crabs, have jointed legs.

The Owl Limpet (*Lottia gigantea*) is a large, 3 inch limpet that makes scars on the soft rocks as it moves in and out of its home area. They return to the home area by following a mucous trail which they secreted as they left in search of food. This limpet is a grazing herbivore, feeding on diatoms and other algae. If you remove the soft body from the shell you will see a scar on the inner surface of the shell which has the shape of an owl in brown colors. This animal is edible, and many carnivores, including man, feed upon it.

Zone III +2.5' to 0.0'

As we continue to move out on the tidal flats, we move into Zone III, which is the mid-tide region. This area is covered for a longer duration each tide than Zone II. It is uncovered by most ebb tides, and covered by most flood tides. This is the zone of the greatest abundance of algae and animals. Most of the plants, and plants from the upper and lower zones also, can be found in

Owl Limpet

profusion (and perhaps confusion) here.
The main algae are the reds and browns.
Unfortunately most of these have no
common name, and the scientific name
is of little value without a complete description; therefore, only the most obvious algae will be described.

The key plant seen in Zone III at
Moss Beach is the Feather Boa Kelp
(*Egregia spp.*). It is a brown algae
growing to more than 30 feet in length.
Egregia looks like a leather strip with
small, leaf-like flaps, and small floats,
or bladders, along the sides. The
Feather Boa, like most brown algae,
attaches to the bottom by a root-like
holdfast. There are 2 species of *Egregia* along our coast. They are *E. menziesii* and *E. laevigata.*

Another common algae is *Halosaccion
glandiforme*. This is a small, red,
bladder or cigar-shaped algae. *Halosaccion glandiforme* is filled with water
that squirts out when the bladder is
squeezed. Some flat, blade-like, red
algae are: *Gigartina* (3-5 species),
which have bumps all over their surface; *Porphyra,* which is very thin and
red (like rubbery onion skin paper); and
Iridaea, which is the algae that shim-
mers in a bluish, purplish iridescence
when under water. There are many
coralline and encrusting algae found
in Zone III. These are very difficult
to key out, but can be identified by
their size and hardness.

The three most common calcified
algae found at Moss Beach are: *Corallina chilensis,* an upright, thin-seg-
mented, branching, plant that grows to
about four inches in length; *Bossea spp.*
which are similar to *Corallina,* but

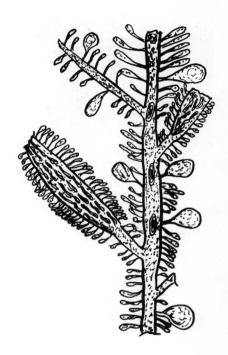

Feather Boa Kelp

Halosaccion spp.

Iridaea spp.

Red Corallina Algae

have broader segments, each with wing-like projections; and *Lithothamnion conchatum* which is the main encrusting algae that covers most of the rocks and shells in this area. All three of these algae are pinkish-red in color. If they are white or fringed with white, they are either dead or dying, and are being bleached by the sun. All of these algae provide food for the grazing molluscs and other herbivores in this zone.

The animals found on the exposed rocks are primarily molluscs, arthropods and coelenterates. One small coelenterate that is abundant in masses on exposed rock surfaces, especially near sand or pebbly areas, is the Sea Anemone (*Anthopleura elegantissima*). This animal has many tentacles that have pink or purplish tips. The body or stalk is greenish and about 2 inches long when expanded. The body is commonly covered with bits of sand and shell that afford it good camouflage. These stones and shells also keep the animal from drying out when the tide is out. Sea anemones eat almost any small animals that can be subdued by the stinging cells imbedded in the anemones' tentacles. These stinging cells (nematocysts) contain a poison which paralyzes the prey. The food is then moved into the mouth and down into the "stomach" area.

The Red Anemone (*Epiactis prolifera*) is a small anemone (about 3/4 inch tall) found on the sides of protected rocks at or under the waterline. There are buds at the base of the body which are actually brood pits that house the young anemones after the breeding season. These animals feed on small fish, crustaceans and worms.

The Brown Turban Snail (*Tegula brunnea*) is one of the most common molluscs in Zone III. They have a heavy shell as does *T. funebralis,* but the shell is light reddish-brown. The brown turban is larger than the black turban (about 1 1/2 - 2 inches tall). These animals are also grazing algae eaters. Some of the *T. brunnea* have a red symbiotic algae, *Peyssonelia,* which is usually found only on these shells. *Peyssonelia* is another encrusting algae.

Brown Turban Snail

The Purple Encrusting Sponges (*Haliclona permollis*) are very common on the edges of channels in the outer rocks and where the surf hits. They feed by filtering microscopic planktonic organisms from the water.

Some soft-bodied oddities are the sea slugs, or Nudibranchs. One such is the Brown-spotted Nudibranch (*Diaulula sandiegensis*) which has dark spots on a tan or cream-colored background. It grows to 1 1/2 inches in length and can be found on the sides of boulders and swimming among the tide pool algae. The anal gills can be seen projecting out of the body when undisturbed. These gills can be retracted if the animal is stimulated. Two other obvious Nudibranchs are the Hopkin's Rose (*Hopkinsia rosacea*), and the Sea Lemon (*Anisodoris nobilis*). The Hopkin's Rose is bright pinkish-red with many dorsal projecting gills. The Sea Lemon is the largest local Nudibranch. It grows to about 8 inches in length and 3 inches in width. The color of this mollusc is bright yellow to bright orange.

Purple Encrusting Sponge

All sea slugs are grazing animals, feeding upon the algae by rasping with

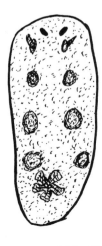

Brown-spotted Nudibranch

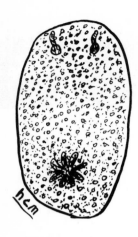

Sea Lemon

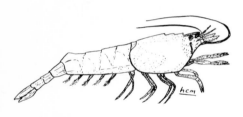

Broken-back Shrimp

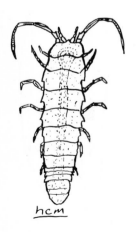

Isopod

a file-like radula. Generally, the projections on the backs of these animals are gills and are used to obtain oxygen. Most Nudibranchs are bright in color and lack shells. The bright colors may be a form of protective coloration called "warning" colors. These animals have a potent acid secretion that is apparently bad-tasting to potential predators.

Many organisms can be found living under rocks in this zone. Turn the rocks over and examine the small pool formed by its removal. In these pools you can find many crustaceans, molluscs, worms, and some brittle stars. After you have noted the life here, replace the rock gently so as not to injure the animals. Some of the organisms common to such pools are discussed below.

The Broken-back Shrimps (*Spirontocaris spp.*) [5-8 local species] are small, shrimp-like animals that have a transparent shell and a green interior. They can be found on the sides of rocks or in the small tidepools in Zones III and IV. The green color is due to their diet of algae. This animal is one of the basic steps in the intertidal food chain. It provides food for many larger carnivores.

Isopods, especially *Idothea urotoma*, are large (up to 2 inches), slow crawling, marine pill bugs that are greenish or brown in color and can be found on the *Egregia* and other dark algae. Let them crawl over your hand to observe their type of locomotion. They are harmless. Like the Broken-back Shrimp, these arthropods are an important source of food for larger carnivores.

Many marine worms can be found in Zone III. Three of the common ones are the mussel worms, the tube worms, and the clam worms. The Mussel Worm (*Lumbrineris zonata*) is a common polycheate (segmented worms with external appendages). It is usually iridescent, greenish-brown, flattened, and has many fins on its side. Beware! Large mussel worms can bite, but rarely do! These animals can usually be found in the sand, under rocks, or among the roots of Eel grass.

The Tube Worms (*Serpula vermicularis*) form twisted, calcareous, whitish tubes that can be found abundantly on the undersurface of the larger rocks. These animals have bright red gills that project from the end of their tubes. Tube Worms and other types of marine worms are filter feeders.

The Clam Worm (*Nereis vexillosa*) is greenish with many segments. It is the largest (up to 12 inches) of the marine worms on this coast, and lives in holes under the rocks. We have actually taken one specimen of this type from Moss Beach which was over 3 feet long and 1 inch in diameter. The tooth-like pinchers are large and dark colored, but are usually inside the mouth. The body is lined with many appendages that are flap-like structures used for locomotion and breathing.

There are many molluscs found under the rocks in this zone, but only two or three have visible holes in their shells. The holes let water out of the shell after the water has passed over the gills. Two gastropods have one hole in the apex of the shell. These

Tube Worms

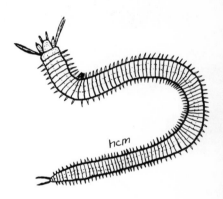

Clam Worm

Keyhole Limpet

are commonly called the Key-hole Limpet and the Volcano Limpet. The larger of the two is *Diodora aspera,* the Keyhole Limpet. It is about two inches long and can be found in Zones III and IV. The gray, ribbed shell has a hole that has one flattened edge if viewed from the inside. These gastropod molluscs are grazing algae eaters and have the radula, as do all snails.

The smaller Volcano Limpet, (*Fissurella volcano*), has an apical opening in a volcano-shaped shell. The shell itself is white with rose-colored lines or rays radiating from the apex. This animal seldom grows in excess of one inch in length.

Occasionally an observer may find a fairly large commensal Polychaete worm (*Arctonöe vittata*) living in the mantle cavity, or gill chamber, of these and other larger molluscs. The size of the commensal worm is dependent upon the size of the host mollusc, and they reach lengths up to 5 inches in abalones and Gum Boot Chitons.

Another mollusc with holes in the shell is the abalone which will be mentioned in the discussion of Zone IV. Chitons, boring clams, and rock oysters will be the last three molluscs to be mentioned in Zone III.

The Pearly Chitons (*Stenoplax spp.*), with 3 local species, have eight dorsal plates, grow to three inches in length, and are usually found under the medium-sized rocks. These animals live in aggregations, and actually have a tendency to move downward on the overturned rocks. This is called negative phototaxis. Remove them and note the foot, gills, and how they curl for protection.

Volcano Limpet

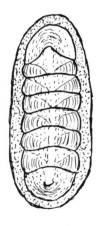

Pearly Chiton

The Mossy Chitons (*Mopalia spp.*),
with 4 local species, are similar to
the Pearly Chitons in size and shell
plate number. Their color, however,
varies from green to black. A distinctive characteristic of Mossy Chitons
is the fringed girdle which appears to
hold the plates in place. These, like
most other chitons, are compressed
dorso-ventrally. Mossy Chitons ex-
hibit a unique "homing" tendency. This
enables them to return to the same rock
depressions for low tides after each
high tide foraging excursion.

Two other smaller (up to 2 inches)
chitons common to our coast are the
Ischnochitons and the *Lepidozonas*.
The shells of these chitons are more
highly arched, and range in color from
red to gray to green. All chitons, with
the possible exception of the "Jockey's
Cap" (*Placiphorella velata*), are grazing
herbivores feeding upon all sorts of algae.

The Rock Oyster (*Hinnites giganteus*), the Jingle Shell (*Pododesmus
macroschisma*), and the Fixed Clam
(*Chama pellucida*) are bivalved molluscs that have one shell glued to some
exposed or partially exposed rock.
These bivalves filter their microscopic
food out of the water using their gills
as a net to catch small organisms. The
shells of these marine organisms range
in size from one inch to several inches.
The color of these shells ranges from
pure white to pink to dark purple. Note
the differences from the drawings.

There are many species of boring
clams along our coasts. Some bore
into the mud, some into the sand, and
some into the rocks found at Moss

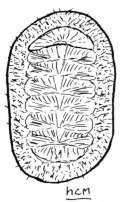

hcm

Mossy Chiton
(*Mopalia sp.*)

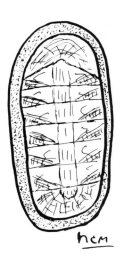

hcm

Butterfly Chiton

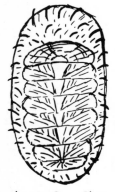

Jockey's Cap Chiton

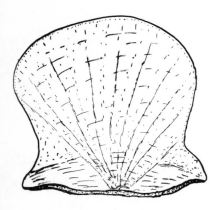

Rock Oyster

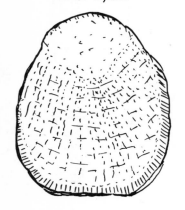

Jingle Shell

Beach. One of the larger and more common boring clams at Moss Beach is the Boring Rock Clam (*Penitella penita*). It has a gray or white shell, and is responsible for many of the holes found in the softer rocks. The young clam settles on the rock, and bores a hole by mechanical and chemical means. The shell may grow to one or two inches in length. Once in the rock, this clam enlarges the bottom of the hole as the animal grows, and is thereby trapped forever. Food is filtered from the water brought into the animal by its long siphon.

Peanut Worms (*Golfingia agassizii*) are boring organisms that are rich brown to slate gray in color. They have long, feathery, oral tentacles on the anterior end that can be retracted into the body. The Peanut Worm grows to about six inches long, but when stimulated it tends to shorten. This animal can be found under rocks or actually bored into the softer rocks. These animals are not true worms.

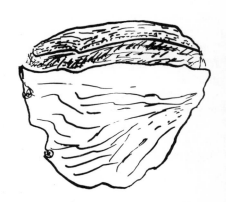

Fixed Clam

There are many other animals found
in this zone that are transients passing
through on their way to higher or lower
zones. Some animals also spend their
larval stages in this zone.

Zone IV 0.0' to −1.6'

The area in Zone IV is exposed by
"minus" tides only, and even then many
areas are partly covered as permanent
tide pools or channels. This area is
the richest in algae and animals, but
is the hardest to get to, and the hardest
to find the organism for which you are
looking. This is also the most dangerous zone. Watch for large waves and
be careful.

In this zone, the algae grow in abundance, but are sometimes difficult to
get and very hard to identify. Several
types are indicator plants for Zone IV.

The Sea Palms (*Postelsia palmaeformis*) can be seen out on the reef
looking like small trees. Sea Palms
have a very rubbery body and a strong
holdfast that allows the plant to exist
in the midst of the breaking surf. These
annual plants have leaf-like structures
that are edible when young.

The Bull Kelp (*Nereocystis luetkeana*)
is the largest algae found along the Central California Coast growing to forty
or fifty feet. *Nereocystis* has a holdfast, a long stem-like structure called
a stipe, and a float which keeps the
leaf-like blades of the plant at or near
the surface. Their long blades extend
from the float. Many fish live among
the kelp beds where they are afforded
protection and food. Both the Sea Palms
and the Bull Kelp are brown algae
(*Phaeophyta*).

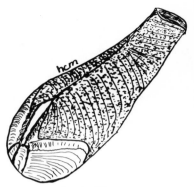

Rock Clam

Peanut Worm

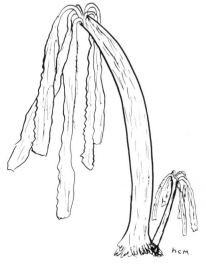

Sea Palm

Many other red and brown algae without common names are generally found in Zone IV. Some of these are *Hymenena, Botryoglossum, Laminaria, Cystoseria,* and *Costaris.* Many other algae from higher zones are also found in this zone. Note the drawings.

The animals that are common to this zone are very interesting, colorful, and many of them are also edible. Only the most obvious, new animals will be mentioned for this zone; however, many animals previously encountered in higher zones may be seen here.

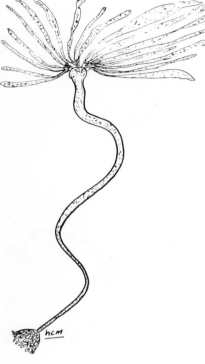

Bull Kelp

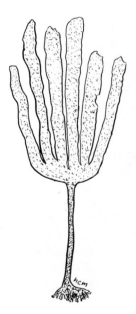

Brown Kelp
(*Laminaria sp.*)

Hymenena sp.

The common Green Sea Anemone (*Anthopleura xanthogrammica*) is the largest Coelenterate found intertidally along our coast. This green anemone grows to a diameter of more than one foot in the deeper pools. This anemone is also found in some permanent tide pools in higher zones. Touch the tentacles with your fingers. The sticky feeling is due to poisonous stinging cells (Nematocysts) which the animal uses to capture its food and to protect itself from enemies.

Costaria sp.

There are many different types of starfish found in Zone IV. The most common is the Ocher or Purple Starfish (*Pisaster ochraceus*). This animal is characteristic of Zones III and IV. The body is flattened, calcified, and usually divided into five rays or arms. Turn this starfish over and note the tube feet with their suckers. The animal uses the tube feet for capturing food and for locomotion.

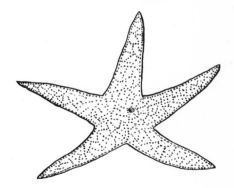

Green Sea Anemone

Cystoseira sp.

Purple Starfish

Other Echinoderms are the sun stars, (with two species of *Solaster* and one species of *Pycnopodia*. They have from 8-15 and 6-24 rays respectively). *P. helianthoides* is the largest, local starfish and is reddish-brown to pink, or purple, usually with a soft body. Many small, immature starfish are found under the rocks in the two lower zones, but they are hard to identify for the beginner.

Red Abalone

Two small identifiable starfish are the small, 6-rayed *Leptasterias aequalis* and the bright red *Henricia leviuscula*. Neither species will grow to over 5 inches in diameter, and they are usually less than 2 1/2 inches across.

The Leather Star (*Dermasterias imbricata*) is a smooth, firm starfish, but unlike most of the other starfish which are carnivorous, eating clams, mussels, chitons, and other molluscs, the Leather Star lives by eating organic debris.

The only common algae-eating starfish is the Sea Bat (*Patiria miniata*). This animal has scale-like plates on its dorsal surface, is red to orange, and the rays (arms) are not distinctly marked from the central disk. These animals are common on the pillars inside the breakwater at Princeton.

Red Starfish

Some of the most conspicuous animals in Zone IV are the Sea Urchins. The Purple Sea Urchin and the large Red Sea Urchin both belong to the same genus. Both are algae eaters, and have spines. White teeth-like structures inside the "ventrally" located mouth are used to cut their food. The larger of the two is the Red Sea Urchin (*Strongylocentrotus franciscanus*). It

has longer spines and is dark red to
blackish in color. The more common
of the two urchins is the Purple Sea
Urchin (*S. purpuratus*). Notice that
these animals live in holes in the rocks.
The animals bore these holes by moving into and out of the "home" area, and
by the action of the spines. Some people eat the gonads of these animals before the animal spawns. Sea urchin
omelets and sea urchins on the half
shell are Sicilian delights. The gonads are largest during the winter
months. The gonads of the females
are orange inside and out while the
male gonad is orange outside and is
milky white inside.

Some interesting molluscs found
in Zone IV are the abalones, and the
Gum Boot Chiton. The Red Abalone
(*Haliotis rufescens*) is the most common and largest abalone, while the
Black Abalone (*H. cracherodii*) is the
smaller and less common along the
peninsula. There are 6 other species
of abalone along our coast but none
are as common as the Red and Black
Abalones. Both have one shell with
numerous holes in it. Both species
can be found in cracks and under the
rocks of this zone. Be careful that
you do not get your fingers under the
shell when the animal decides to hold
on. A license and a marked tire iron
are necessary to acquire these good
tasting molluscs.

The Gum Boot Chiton (*Cryptochiton
stelleri*) is the world's largest chiton.
There are more than one hundred species of chitons along our coast. It
grows to over 16 inches in length and
looks like one-half of a red, velvety

Leather Star
Oral view

Sea Bat

Red Sea Urchin

Red Abalone

Black Abalone

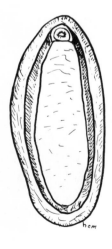

Gumboot Chiton

football. The eight plates characteristic of all chitons are internal. Turn
the animal over and look in the mantle
groove. Note the gills, and look for
the commensual scale worms that may
live there. The most common commensual worm is *Arctonöe vittata*.

The red, or orange, coral (*Balanophyllia elegans*) is the only coral found
intertidally at Moss Beach. The skele-
ton is calcified, but the body looks like
a small orange or yellow sea anemone
and is soft. These animals are found
in cracks and under ledges where the
surf can bring them food. They have
tentacles with stinging cells just like
all anemones. These corals grow to
about 1/6 inch in diameter and are usually solitary.

Zone IV has several common sponges
that are identified by their color, body
softness, and by openings or pores in
their surface. These pores are for the
passage of water and food through the
animal. Sponges feed by filtering their
food from this water. They are the
Yellow-boring Sponge (*Cliona celata*),
the Purple-encrusting Sponge (*Haliclona permollis*), and the Red-encrusting
Sponge (*Ophlitaspongia pennata*). None
of these sponges are of commercial
value because of their small size and
brittleness.

Note that the Sea Weed Limpet (*Acmaea incessa*) is only found on the sea
weeds, usually the Feather Boa Kelp
(*Egregia*). Sea Weed Limpets eat the
algae on which they are found, and form
oblong scars where the animals can be
easily found. The shell is brown,
smooth, and has a high apex. This
animal may grow to 3/4 inch in length.

The main large crabs in Zone IV are the Kelp Crabs and the Cancer Crabs. The Kelp Crab (*Pugettia producta*) has a smooth, hard, shield-shaped body and ten reddish legs. The male crabs turn bright red during the breeding season but are normally reddish-brown. The front pair of legs have pinchers, but they are not too dangerous. This crab is slow moving and is often found clinging tenaciously to kelp or other sea weeds. Be careful of the spines on the tips of the legs, because this animal can puncture the skin if carelessly handled. These crabs actually build a nest by intertwining blades of the Feather Boa Kelp.

Cancer Crabs (*Cancer productus* and *C. antennarius*) are large, reddish crabs and are edible. There are several other species found along our coast, and all of the larger ones have a carapace which grows to more than 6 inches across.

The undersurface is lighter red and has darker red spots. These animals have large, heavy pinchers, and should be handled carefully.

The Cancer Crabs are harvested by commercial fisheries and sold in many markets on the San Mateo Peninsula. The Cancer Crabs are omnivorous, eating almost any plant or animal materials. They in turn are food for larger fish, the sea gulls and, of course, the Octopus.

The Octopus (*Octopus spp.*) is a not-so-common, under-rock dweller of our intertidal area. It is widely hunted along this coast as a food animal, and is now becoming rare. Note the large eyes, the tentacles with their suckers,

top view

Solitary Coral

Kelp Bass

side view

Seaweed Limpet

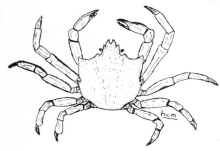

Kelp Crab

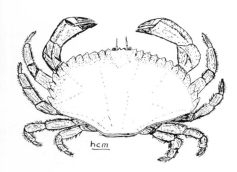

Cancer Crab

Octopus and Mr. Williams

and the ability of this animal to conceal itself. Concealment may be accomplished by changing color rapidly, or by spewing dark clouds of inky material. This animal has a beak like a parrot, but is not considered dangerous unless the animal is fairly large. The eight tentacles are lined with sucker-like discs. These help in capturing food and in locomotion. All octopods belong to the mollusc grouping called the Cephalopods which includes squids, cuttlefish, and the poetic chambered nautilus.

Looking seaward from Zone IV several types of birds can be seen feeding, and/or floating on the waves, or on the exposed rocks. Sea gulls, ducks, and cormorants make up the bulk of these birds.

The Surf Scoter (*Melanitta perspicillata*) is a black, duck-like bird that can be seen diving and feeding on various bottom foods (mussels, clams, etc.) in the white water where the waves are breaking. The male Surf Scoter has white patches on the front and back of its head, while the female is more brownish with the white patches in front of and behind the eyes. The Surf Scoter is smaller (17 inches long) than the White-winged Scoter (*Melanitta deglandi*) and lacks the wing patches possessed by the latter bird.

The Black, or Common Scoter (*Oidemia nigra*) is all black, and has an orange bill. All of these birds eat fish and marine plants. Note that they dive under water just before the waves break on them, and they also hold their wings up when they land on the water.

The Pacific Brown Pelican (*Pelaca-nus occidentalis*) is a large, slow flying bird with brownish feathers, a white head, and a large bill. These birds nest at Point Lobos as well as on other protected points and islands along the coast. The large bill and neck pouch are used in catching and holding fish. You can see these pelicans flying in neat lines close to the water using slow wing beats. They can also be seen sitting passively on rocks and bouys, with their heads held erect and their bills against their chest.

There are three species of comor-ants along the San Mateo coast. They are the Double Crested Comorant (*Pha-lacrocorax auritus*), Brandt's Comorant (*P. penicillatus*), and the Pelagic, or Baird's Comorant (*P. pelagicus*). The first two birds are larger than ducks, having bodies exceeding thirty inches in length, and wingspans of about 36 inches. Both of these birds have long necks with yellow and brownish-blue throat pouches respectively. They fly with rapid wing motion close to the water. These are the birds with snake-like necks that sit upright on rocks. All comorants are fish eaters. In China birds like these are used to catch fish for man. The Baird's comorant is much smaller than the other two, has a thinner bill, a white patch on the side near the tail and has a dull red neck patch.

This partial list of birds does not include many other birds which may be seen at the beach like the myriads of ducks and geese during the migra-tory season. Nor does it mention many birds like the Terns, Oystercatchers,

Surf Scoter

White-winged Scoter

Common Scoter

Brown Pelican

Double-crested Cormorant

Phalaropes, and Murres. Any good book of western water fowl will serve this purpose. See the included drawings.

A few interesting mammals that are common to the Central California Coast either as residents or as migrants are the California Grey Whale, Killer Whale, Porpoise, Elephant Seal, California Sea Lion, and the Harbor Seals.

The last three animals breed at Año Nuevo Island, and are frequent visitors to breakwaters, offshore islands, and many other areas along our coast. All are protected by Federal and International Law, and should never be harmed.

Baird's Cormorant

Caspian Tern

Forester's Tern

The California Grey Whale (*Es-chrichtius glaucus*) reaches lengths from 32 to 55 feet and is mottled grey in color. It has a slightly humped back which lacks the dorsal fin character-istic of the Killer Whale. The Grey Whale migrates from the North Pacific southward past central California each winter in December and January. They migrate close to shore to their breeding grounds in Scammods Lagoon in Baja California. When they reach their breeding area, the female gives birth to a single calf that is from 12–16 feet long. Soon after giving birth, the whales mate and in May they start the trip back to Arctic waters. The calf is weaned in 7–8 months.

Phalaropes

Murres

Oystercatcher

Coot

These large and interesting mammals can be seen spouting and swimming along our shores feeding on Krill (planktonic amphipods and small shrimp-like crustaceans) or in shallow waters, feeding on sardines.

The most common whale seen off the California coast is the Common Finback Whale (*Balaenoptera physalus*) which grows to 80 feet in length. It is brownish above, white below (not mottled, as is the Grey Whale), and has a small dorsal fin well back on the body. This is another filter-feeding Baleen Whale.

Three members of the Delphinidae family are visitors to the Bay Area. Two are porpoises, and one is the Killer Whale.

Our Killer Whale (*Orcinus orca*) grows to 30 feet in length and is the most vicious killer in the ocean. They are characterized by having black bodies with white patches behind their eyes and white lower jaws and bellies. The dorsal fin is tall and straight. These killers have 44 large, conical teeth, and a huge appetite. The Killer Whales hunt in a pack and feed on seals, sea lions, fishes, and even on the California Grey Whale. Both of these whales are frequent visitors to Monterey Bay and other West Coast areas that have a good sea mammal population.

The Bay, or harbor, and Dall Porpoises (*Phocaena phocoena* and *Phocoenoides dalli*) are 5 to 7 feet long, fish-eating mammals occasionally seen along this coast or in San Francisco Bay. The Bay Porpoise is black, has a lighter belly, and a

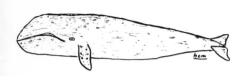

California Grey Whale

Common Finback Whale

Killer Whale

triangular dorsal fin. The Dall Porpoise is slightly larger, jet black with
a large shiny white patch on its side,
and it also has a triangular dorsal fin.

Three marine mammals breed or
are very numerous within the geographic confines of San Mateo County. They
are the Northern Elephant Seal (*Mirounga angustirostris*), the Harbor
Seal (*Phoca vitulina*), and the California Sea Lion (*Zalophus californianus*).
All three can be found at Año Nuevo
Point and Año Nuevo Island in San Mateo
County. Other breeding sites for seals
and sea lions are protected points and
breakwaters, like the one at Monterey,
California. They can also be found on
many offshore islands along the coast
north of Año Nuevo Point and on large
islands like the Farallons and on the
Channel Islands off southern California.
The range of all three animals is generally from Mexican waters to Washing-
ton. These are not the only pinnipedes
found on our coast, but are the most
common.

The Northern Elephant Seal is the
largest of the seal group. A large
male may grow to 15–17 feet and weigh
2,000 pounds or more. The males are
dull gray with brownish fur and are
easily identified by a large, inflatable
nose or proboscis. These animals
lack external ears. The females are
smaller, 7–8 feet, and have brown fur.
Like the whales, the females give birth
to one pup each, usually in December.
The female suckles the young, at least
until the breeding season in March.
Shortly after giving birth and suckling,
they are mated by a dominant bull seal.
The Elephant Seal probably feeds upon

Bay Porpoise

Dall Porpoise

Elephant Seal

fish, squid, and small sharks. The large sharks and Killer Whales, in turn, feed upon all three of these Pinnipedia. However, man is the greatest danger to these organisms.

Another seal found all along our coast in protected harbors and bays is the Harbor Seal. It is only 4-5 feet long, is earless, and has a grayish body with white, yellowish or darkish spots. Like the Northern Elephant Seal, the back flippers are always extended behind and they cannot be brought up alongside the body. This seal, like the Elephant Seal, can not climb very well over the rocks and ledges and is, therefore, restricted to the beaches and cove areas where it can "haul out." The Harbor Seal feeds on fish, squid, and crustaceans. Unlike the majority of other seals, the Harbor Seal does not form harems, but they are polygamous. The mating season is from winter to early spring or immediately after the birth of one pup seal.

60"

Harbor Seal

Another common marine mammal we will mention is the California Sea Lion (this is the familiar "trained seal"). The male sea lion reaches a length of 8 feet and a weight of nearly 600 pounds, while the female only reaches 6 feet and about 300 pounds. The males are dark brown, and have a protruding crest on their forehead, while the females are light brown.

California Sea Lion

All sea lions can move the back flipper under the body, enabling them to move over the rocks and climb cliffs with more ease than the first two animals mentioned. During the breeding season (May-August) the largest and strongest males gather a harem of several "cow" sea lions. The pups are born about one year after mating. The sea lions feed primarily upon small fish and squid which they capture with their rapid, underwater speed.

The Steller's Sea Lion (*Eumetopias jubata*) is also fairly common along our coast. The males are large (7-10 feet and 800 pounds) and have a crest on the forehead. They are brown and have a thick coating of fur. The females are only 4-6 feet long and weigh some 200 pounds.

These animals and plants discussed for the central California coast are by no means the only ones you may encounter, but they will be the most common. These animals and their surrounding algae will give the beginner some appreciation of the life along our coast.

Steller's Sea Lion

Steller's Sea Lion

Surf Perch

Rock Bass

A Check List of the Central California Coastal
Plants and Animals

Those organisms with the asterisks are mentioned in this chapter.

Plants

* Monterey Pine (*Pinus radiata*)
* Monterey Cypress (*Cupressus macrocarpa*)
* Blue Beach Lupine (*Lupinus chamissionis*)
* Tree Lupine (*Lupinus arboreus*)
* California Blackberry (*Rubus vitifolius*)
* Coastal Salt Bush (*Atriplex leucophylla*)
* New Zealand Spinach (*Tetragonia expansa*)
* Sweet Alyssum (*Alyssum maritimum*)
* Mustards (*Brassica spp.*, *Capsella spp.*)
  Beach Morning Glory (*Convolvulus soldanella*)
* Hottentot Fig (*Mesembryanthemum edule*)
* Sea Fig (*M. chilense*)
* Ice Plant (*M. floribundum*)
* Eel Grass (*Zostera marina*)
* Surf Grass (*Phyllospadix torreyi*), (*Phyllospadix scouleri*)
* German Ivy (*Senecio mikanioides*)

For more land plants see the chapters on the Grasslands and the
Chaparral.

Algae

* Yellowish Green Algae (*Enteromorpha intestinalis*)
* Rock Weeds (*Fucus*; *Pelvetiopsis*)
* Brown Algae (*Ralfsia sp.*)
* Red Algae (*Endocladia muricata*)
* Red Rock Weed (*Gigartina cristata*)
* Sea Lettuce (*Ulva spp.*)
* Mermaid's Pin Cushion (*Cladophora trichotoma*)
* *Corallina chilensis*; *Bossea spp.*; *Lithothamnian conchatum*
* *Grateloupia spp.*; *Prionitis spp.*
* Feather Boa Kelp (*Egregia menziesii*)
* *Halosaccion glandiforme*; *Gigartina*; *Porphyra*; *Iridaea*
* Sea Palm (*Postelsia palmaeformis*)
* Bull Kelp (*Nereocystis leutkeana*)
* *Hymenena spp.*; *Botryoglossum spp.*; *Laminaria*; *Cystoseira*;
   Costaris
* *Peyssonelia sp.*

Fish (Intertidal and Coastal)

* Black Prickleback *(Epigeichthys atropurpureus)*
* Rockweed Gunnel *(Xererpes fucorum)*
* Rock Pool Blenny *(Hypsoblennius gilberti)*
* Sculpins *(Clinocottus spp.; Oligocottus spp.)*
* Clingfish *(Sicyogaster meandrica)*
  Johnny Sculpin *(Oligocottus maculosus)*
  Wooly Sculpin *(Clinocottus analis)*
  Reef Finspot *(Paraclinus integripinnis)*
  Crevice Klipfish *(Gibbsonia montereyensis)*
  Monkey Face Eel *(Cebidichthys violaceus)*
  Cabezon *(Scorpaenichthys marmoratus)*
  Greenling Sea Trout *(Hexagrammos decagrammus)*
  Rockfish *(Sebastodes spp.)*
  Surf Perches *(Amphistichus spp.)*
  Striped Bass *(Roccus saxatilis)*

Birds

* California Gull *(Larus californicus)*
* Ring-billed Gull *(Larus delawarensis)*
* Western Gull *(Larus occidentalis)*
* Herring Gull *(Larus argentatus)*
* Killdeer *(Charadrius vociferus)*
* Spotted Sand Piper *(Actitis macularia)*
* Surf Scoter *(Melanitta perspicillata)*
* White-winged Scoter *(Melanitta deglandi)*
* Black Scoter *(Oidemia nigra)*
* Pacific Brown Pelican *(Pelacanus occidentalis)*
* Double Crested Comorant *(Phalacrocorax auritus)*
* Brandt's Comorant *(P. penicillatus)*
* Baird's Comorant *(P. pelagicus)*
  Common Murre *(Uria aalge)*
  Phalaropes *(Phalaropus sp., Steganopus sp., Lobipes sp.)*
  Oyster Catcher *(Haematopus bachmani)*

For more birds common in this area see the chapter on The Bay and
Salt Marsh.

Mammals

* California Grey Whale (*Eschrichtius glaucus*)
* Common Finback Whale (*Balaenoptera physalus*)
* Killer Whale (*Orcinus orca*)
* Bay Porpoise (*Phocaena phocoena*)
* Dall Porpoise (*Phocoenoides dalli*)
* Elephant Seal (*Mirounga angustirostris*)
* Harbor Seal (*Phoca vitulina*)
* California Sea Lion (*Zalophus californianus*)
* Stellar's Sea Lion (*Eumetopias jubata*)

Invertebrates

* Beach Hopper (*Orchestoidea californiana*)
* Pill Bug (*Ligia occidentalis*)
* Periwinkles (*Littorina planaxis*)
* Common Rock Limpet (*Acmaea digitalis*)
* Ribbed Limpet (*Acmaea scabra*)
* Acorn Barnacles (*Balanus glandula*)
* Brown Barnacle (*Chthamalus dalli*)
* Red Copepod (*Tigriopus californicus*)
  Sand Dollar (*Dendraster excentricus*)
* Periwinkle (*Littorina scutulata*)
* Unicorn (*Acanthina spirata*)
* Rock Snail (*Thais emarginata*)
* Black Turban Snail (*Tegula funebralis*)
* Purple Shore Crab (*Hemigrapsus nudus*)
* Lined Shore Crab (*Pachygrapsus crassipes*)
* Porcelain Crab (*Petrolisthes cinctipes*)
* Flat Crab (*Pachycheles rudis*)
* Hermit Crab (*Pagurus samuelis*)
* Hairy Hermit Crab (*Pagurus hirsutiusculus*)
* Purple Olive Shells (*Olivella biplicata*)
* Brittle Stars (*Ophioplocus esmarki*; *Ophiothrix spiculata*; *Amphiodia occidentalis*)
* Flatworms (*Notoplana acticola*; *Alloioplana californica*)
* Hairy-gilled Worms (*Cirriformia luxuriosa*)
* Circle Serpulids (*Spirorbis spp.*)
* Wigglers (*Melita palmata*; *Elasmopus rapax*)
* California Mussels (*Mytilus californianus*)
* Mossy Chiton (*Mopalia muscosa*)

Invertebrates (continued)

* Butterfly Chitons (*Ischnochiton regularis*); (*Lepidozona spp.*)
* Red Barnacle (*Tetraclita squamosa rubescens*)
* Goose-neck Barnacles (*Pollicipes polymerus*)
* Owl Limpet (*Lottia gigantea*)
* Sea Anemone (*Anthopleura elegantissima*)
* Red Anemone (*Epiactis prolifera*)
* Brown Turban (*Tegula brunnea*)
* Black Turban (*T. funebralis*)
* Purple Sponge (*Haliclona permollis*)
* Hopkin's Rose (*Hopkinsia rosacea*)
* Sea Lemon (*Anisodoris nobilis*)
* Broken Back Shrimp (*Spirontocaris spp.*)
* Isopods (*Idothea spp.*)
* Mussel Worm (*Lumbrineris zonata*)
* Tube Worm (*Serpula vermicularis*)
* Clam Worm (*Nereis vexillosa*)
* Key Hole Limpet (*Diodora aspera*)
* Volcano Limpet (*Fissurella volcano*)
* Pearly Chiton (*Stenoplax spp.*)
* Jockey Cap (*Placiphorella velata*)
* Rock Oyster (*Hinnites giganteus*)
* Jingle Shell (*Pododesmus macroschisma*)
* Fixed Clam (*Chama pellucida*)
* Boring Rock Clam (*Penitella penita*)
* Peanut Worm (*Golfingia Agassizi*) (*Phascolosoma*)
* Green Sea Anemone (*Anthopleura xanthogrammica*)
* Ocher Starfish (*Pisaster ochraceus*)
* Sun Stars (*Solaster*; *Pycnopodia*; *P. helianthoides*)
* Starfish (*Lepasterias aequalis*; *Henricia leviuscula*)
* Leather Star (*Dermasterias imbricata*)
* Sea Bat (*Patiria miniata*)
* Red Sea Urchin (*Strongylocentrotus franciscanus*)
* Purple Sea Urchin (*S. purpuratus*)
* Red Abalone (*Haliotis rufescens*)
* Black Abalone (*H. cracherodii*)
* Gum Boot Chiton (*Cryptochiton stelleri*)
* Commensual Worm (*Arctonoë vittata*)
* Orange (Red) Coral (*Balanophyllia elegans*)
* Yellow Boring Sponge (*Cliona celata*)
* Purple Encrusting Sponge (*Haliclona permollis*)

Invertebrates (continued)

* Red Encrusting Sponge *(Ophlitasponsia pennata)*
* Sea Weed Limpet *(Acmaea incessa)*
* Kelp Crab *(Pugettia producta)*
* Cancer Crab *(Cancer productus; C. antennarius)*
* Octopus *(Octopus spp.)*

Grouper

Goosenecked Barnacle and
California Mussel

Field Exercise #3

Name _____

Score _____

Plants

List the identifiable land plants observed on the way to the "beach."

1.   6.

2.   7.

3.   8.

4.   9.

5.   10.

List by zone the common plants and animals noted on this field trip.

Zone I   Plants   Animals

1.   1.   6.

2.   2.   7.

3.   3.   8.

4.   4.   9.

5.   5.   10.

Zone II   Plants   Animals

1.   1.   6.

2.   2.   7.

3.   3.   8.

4.   4.   9.

5.   5.   10.

Field Exercise #3 (continued)

Zone III   Plants

1.
2.
3.
4.
5.

Animals

1.   6.
2.   7.
3.   8.
4.   9.
5.   10.

Zone IV   Plants

1.
2.
3.
4.
5.

Animals

1.   6.
2.   7.
3.   8.
4.   9.
5.   10.

List the shore birds observed on this trip.

1.   6.   11.
2.   7.   12.
3.   8.   13.
4.   9.   14.
5.   10.   15.

Field Exercise #4   Name_____

                                     Score_____

   Discuss the environmental factors that control the plants and animals characteristic of any one tidal zone.

   Discuss the causes and controls of the tides.

CHAPARRAL

One of the most characteristic biomes of the Pacific Coastal region is the chaparral. The derivation of the term "chaparral" is the Spanish word "chaparro," or scrub oak. This is a small, gnarled member of the oak family that grows in dry coastal and foothill regions, and is typical of the vegetation found in this biome. There are actually two types of chaparral found throughout the Northern California coastal area; the coastal chaparral and the high chaparral. The coastal chaparral is most common to the Bay Area, so our discussion will focus on this sub-biome, but mention will be made where obvious differences occur. Typical coastal chaparral can be seen in the Crystal Springs Water Shed and along the slopes of the Santa Cruz ranges. High chaparral can be seen best in the Pinnacles National Monument and the Los Padros National Forest, in Monterey County.

Geologic features of an area do not necessarily restrict or determine chaparral occurrence, but we can note several common physical characteristics of most chaparral regions. Generally, the areas of low, shrubby growth are close to marine coasts, or their coastal influence. The soil is usually shallow and rocky. Humus and leaf litter is scarce. Winters are generally short, cool and wet. This represents the growing season of chaparral plants. The summers are usually devoid of rain. Temperatures are high, and evaporation from the soil and vegetation is excessive. During the long, hot, dry summers, the plants are almost dormant. This results in an overall short growing season and long periods of inactivity.

Due to the high rate of summer evaporation in chaparral zones, most plants have small, thick, dry leaves, and small flowers. The stems are woody and gnarled. This extremely dry condition coupled with long, hot summers make chaparral regions very susceptible to burn offs, or shrub fires. If you visit this area during the dry months, be especially careful of smoking or campfires.

Because of the prevailing winds and soil characteristics, coastal chaparral is usually found on the Eastern (leeward) slopes of our coast ranges. The Western (windward) slopes are usually covered with grasses and flowers. These grassy areas will be discussed later under the separate heading of Grasslands or Savanna. The demarcation line between grasslands and chaparral is usually quite distinct, and most often is found right at the crest of the hill or ridge.

The abruptness of these changes makes it difficult to "chart a path" through the chaparral. Consequently, we find ourselves in the biome surrounded with its organisms without any forewarning. It will, therefore, be impractical for us to attempt to walk through this biome as we did the first two. We will, instead, just describe the organisms most likely to be encountered.

Coast Live Oak

Hoary Manzanita

Of the four species of oaks common to our chaparral, the Leather Oak (*Quercus durata*) and the Interior Live Oak (*Q. wislizenii*) are the less common, and therefore will not be mentioned.

Scrub Oak (*Quercus dumosa*) is a densely growing shrubby-tree with short, branching stems. The bark is a scaly, light gray. The short, deeply serrated leaves are rather stiff and curled inward. The serrated edges have sharp spines. The fruit is typical oak acorn. The "tree" seldom exceeds 8 feet in height.

The Coast Live Oak (*Quercus agrifolia*) is one of the most widely distributed broadleaf trees growing along the coastal ranges. It is taller than the scrub oaks, and possesses a typical main trunk growing up into the crown of secondary limbs. Perhaps the most significant identifying feature is the curling nature of the leaf edges. This tends to form shallow bowls or cups out of each spiked leaf. The presence of the Coast Live Oak in the chaparral indicates a slightly more moist and deeper soil.

There are 40 species of Manzanita in California, but only 15 are common to our peninsula and 7 are found in the San Mateo chaparral. The Hoary Manzanita (*Arctostaphylos canescens*) is a gnarled, woody shrub 6-8 feet in height with small grayish-green leaves on the outermost portions of the stems.

This portion of the limbs may be covered
with a gray, fuzzy material or pubescence. The older, inner portions of the
stems, lose this fuzzy material, and
have a dark red, smooth appearance.
Its berries, when green, can be made
into a drink. The ripe reddish-brown
berries can be eaten fresh. The seeds
can be dried, beaten and made into a
flour for cakes or bread. This plant
is found most typically in the high
chaparral.

Chamise (*Adenostoma fasciculatum*),
or Grease Wood, is a small (3-4 foot)
shrub with short (1/2 inch) needle-like
leaves in bunches arranged about the
stem. It produces a small, white,
vase-like flower in the early spring.
This plant gets its name from the high
oil content and its burning ability.

Coffee Berry (*Rhamus californica*)
is a 4-6 foot bush with serrated, leathery leaves that are shiny underneath
and dark green on top. The greenish
flowers are produced in groups or
bunches on a single stem. The berries
produced by these flowers turn red
then black. The bark of this plant is
dark reddish-brown. The dried berries
can be ground and made into a coffee-
like drink.

Buck-Brush (*Ceanothus cuneatus*)
reaches a height of 10 to 12 feet. The
small, light green leaves are almost
white underneath. During the spring
months, this shrub produces bunches
of flowers that have a pleasant fra-
grance. After the flowers wilt, the
fruit develops into small (1/2 inch)
capsules with short projections on the
end away from the stem. There are
many types of Ceanothus, or Lilac,

Chamise

Coffee Berry

Buck Brush

Toyon (Christmas) Berry

Poison Oak

Coyote Bush

found in the chaparral. The flowers may be blue as well as white depending upon the species of the plant.

Christmas Berry, or Toyon (*Photinia arbutifolia*) grows to a 15' height in moist areas of the chaparral. The 4" serrated leaves are dark green and shiny. The small, white flowers give way to red berries in bunches near the tips of the branches. These bright bunches of berries can be picked and roasted. While they can be eaten raw, cooking tends to remove the slight bitter taste. The red berries may be used for decorative purposes as is the fruit of holly or bittersweet.

Poison Oak (*Rhus diversiloba*) is usually a low (4'-5'), sparse bush that loses its leaves during the winter, but produces a tri-folate (three leaflets) compound leaf on a relatively long petiole or stem. The leaflets are green, oily, and shiny in the spring, but turn red and dryer during late summer and fall. The small, green flowers produce hanging bunches of white shiny fruit. The long fibers were woven into baskets, and the juices used for black dyes by the California Indians. We hasten to add that this was done only after immunity had been built up in the individuals concerned. Several deaths have been reported in California due to poisonings by this plant. Be careful in handling these plants.

Coyote Bush (*Baccharis pilularis*) is another low shrub of the chaparral particularly found along road cuts and broken earth. The small (1/2"-1") serrated leaf resembles a small oak leaf. When the Coyote Bush is in

bloom, it produces a small white flower in vase-like pods. This bush is one
of the most common plants on the San
Francisco Peninsula, and can be found
in nearly all of the dryer biomes.

California Laurel, or Bay (*Umbellularia californica*) is a tree with long,
dark green leaves that have a distinct,
pleasant odor when crushed. The oils
exuding from fallen leaves prevent most
ground covers from growing underneath
the spread of the plant. The thin-shelled
nuts have been parched or roasted in
open fires, and then cracked and eaten.
They can also be ground up and made
into a form of bread. The pleasant
smelling leaves are used for cooking
as a seasoning. They can also be used
as a tea.

Spearmint (*Mentha spicata*) is a
small bush yielding a fine growth of
mint that is used as a flavoring in
everything from chewing gum to juleps.
This grows along road cuts and in
shaded gullies in the chaparral areas.

Spanish Bayonet (*Yucca spp.*) is
common in the southern or high chaparral. A few can be found on the peninsula generally in southern areas. Cloth,
sandals, and ropes can be made from
the fibers, the split leaves, or the entire leaves of this plant. The leaves
must first be soaked in water, then be
pounded to break down the long, hard
fibers. This was probably the most
important fiber plant used by the Indians
and early settlers in California. It is
in greatest abundance in high chaparral
regions, and should be approached
carefully wherever it is found. Its
long slender leaves are tipped with
hard, extremely sharp points.

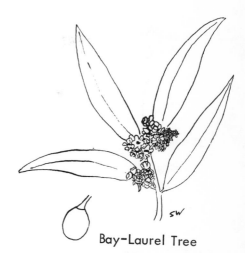

Bay-Laurel Tree

Mint

Spanish Bayonet

Many other Grassland or Savanna plants are also common to these chaparral areas and the next chapter should be consulted for some of the wild flowers, grasses and bushes which "overlap" from these other dry areas.

white

Yarrow

Chaparral Broom

Mammals

Male Mule Deer

The Mule Deer, or Black-tailed Deer, *(Odocoileus hemionus)* is a very wary animal that depends upon speed and agility to escape its enemies. However, when cornered or wounded, the large adult males become very dangerous adversaries. More hunters are killed by wounded deer in the United States than by any other wild animal. The antlers are shed each year in late winter, but grow back even larger by early spring. Contrary to popular belief, however, the oldest bucks do not have the broadest spread of antlers.

For some reason, once the male has passed his sexual prime, his ability to produce the magnificent "horns" declines, and he may have even fewer points than younger, more "robust" bucks. Deer are browsers, feeding in the early morning or late afternoon on the leaves of chaparral bushes or grasses.

The Mountain Lion, Cougar, or "panther" (*Felis concolor*) is the largest member of the cat family still roaming the wilds in the United States. The main diet of this animal is the deer, and as a general rule, wherever there are deer, there are cougars. The Cougar, or Mountain Lion, usually selects only the sick or lame deer for its meals because of its inability to "run down" the mature, healthy members of the deer herd, and an apparent reluctance to engage in combat with the dangerous antlers of the adult male deer. This "choice" of the sick and the lame is in contrast to the human hunter who can pull down his prey with a well-aimed .30.06 slug from a safe 300 yards.

Cougar

Bobcat or Wildcat (*Lynx rufus*) are also found in the chaparral areas. The major source of food for the feisty, short-tailed Bobcat is the rodent family. This selection of food makes the Bobcat an important factor in rodent control. While this cat can be dangerous if cornered or wounded, it usually attempts every possible means of escape first. This animal, like the Cougar, is an important carnivore in the ecological picture of the peninsula. Its tufted ears and short tail are diagnostic characteristics of the Bobcat.

Bobcat

Coyote

Grey Fox

Beechey Ground Squirrel

The Coyote (*Canis latrans*) is a member of the dog family and is another important pest control factor in our environment. While it is true that the Coyote does occasionally dine on domestic fowl, its main dietary supply is made up of the harmful Jack Rabbit, the disease-carrying ground squirrel, gophers, mice, and rats. Unlike the Cougar and Bobcat, which seem to prefer the forested areas, the Coyote prefers the open, grassy areas. They make their "den" either by excavation, or by taking over a hollow log. Most of these beneficial animals, along with the Cougar and Bobcats, have been eliminated from the peninsula by misguided "sportsmen" or "varmint" hunters.

Another member of the dog family, which is of great importance in pest control, is the Grey Fox (*Urocyon cinereoargenteus*). Its fur is coarse and of no commercial value, but it "pays its way" many times over each year in mouse and rat control. These animals can frequently be seen at night all along Skyline Boulevard. Its short legs, pointed nose, and long, fluffy tail set it apart from domestic dogs.

The California Ground Squirrel, or "Beechey" Ground Squirrel (*Otospermophilus* [*Citellus*] *beecheyi*) is a grayish-brown squirrel with a lighter whitish-gray mantle. It is a major reservoir of the plague-causing organism in the San Francisco Bay Area. The "Beechey" Ground Squirrel does thousands of dollars worth of damage to agricultural crops each year. This animal feeds primarily upon the young green sprouts of grasses and grains.

They also eat the tender roots of commercial food crops. During the dry summer season, many of them go into their ground burrows and have a summer-long sleep, or aestivation, which is the summer rendition of winter hibernation.

Norway Rats (*Rattus norvegicus*)were the animals that brought the "Black Death" to Europe in the 14th and 15th Centuries which ultimately resulted in the deaths of over one third of the population of that continent. In California, these rats not only act as disease carrying agents, but they also contaminate millions of dollars worth of food each year. Unlike most rodents, the Norway Rat will live in close proximity with humans, sharing their food, sewers, shelter and at times, even their beds. He is distinguished from the more harmless pack rat or Wood Rat(*Neotoma fuscipes*)by having a darker, coarser hair than its less obnoxious cousin. The rat's main enemies in nature are the Coyote, Bobcat, fox, hawks and owls.

The Trowbridge Shrew (*Sorex trowbridgii*) is the smallest mammal in the Bay Area. It varies in length from two and a half inches to two and three quarters inches. Even though the shrew is small, it has a huge appetite which can, fortunately, only be satisfied by a continuous supply of insects. Shrews can usually be found scrounging around under fallen leaves and other ground debris. The animal has a sharp, pointed, hairy snout for ferreting out its prey.

Norway Rat

Wood Rat

Trowbridge Shrew

Ringtailed Cat

Pinyon Mouse

Reptiles and Amphibians

Rattlesnake

Common Kingsnake

The Western Rattlesnake (*Crotalus viridis*) is a small rattlesnake and is the only poisonous snake found in the San Francisco Bay Area. It seldom reaches a length of over four feet, and is quite secretive and elusive in its habits. It will strike, however, if stepped upon or picked up. The poison injected by the bite of a rattlesnake acts primarily upon the blood cells of the victim resulting in some pain, swelling and usually shock of varying degrees. Fewer than thirty deaths occur each year throughout the entire United States as a direct result of rattlesnake bite, and most of these occur in the southeastern and southwestern states where the rattlesnakes reach very large proportions, and become increasingly irritable.

The Western Rattlesnake, while of no great danger to man, acts as another important check on the rodent population in this area. These snakes are fairly numerous particularly in the drier areas. They give birth to their young rather than laying eggs, and the newly-born rattlesnake is capable of striking and injecting venom. Distinguishing characteristics of this snake are its triangular head, very thin neck, rather fat body with diamond-shaped pattern, and several dry rattles at the tip of the tail. One rattle is added every time the snake sheds its skin.

The Common Kingsnake (*Lampropeltis getulus*) is best known for its attacks on the Rattlesnake. Its main diet, however, consists of other snakes and lizards. Rattlesnakes apparently recognize the Kingsnake, and attempt every possible means of escape. The Kingsnake is immune to the venom of the Rattlesnake, and usually responds aggressively in the presence of the poisonous snake. The Kingsnake is a constrictor, and kills its prey by grasping it by the neck and squeezing it to death. Some records indicate that the Kingsnake can swallow other snakes whole even though the victim exceeds the Kingsnake in length. The Kingsnake has alternating black and yellowish-white bands covering the entire length of the body. They range in length from 2-4 feet.

Gopher Snake

The Gopher Snake (*Pituophis catenifer*), as the name implies, eats gophers, mice, rats, moles, and other small mammals. It is a constrictor, killing its prey by coiling around it and squeezing. The Gopher Snakes tend to be somewhat hostile, and occasionally bite furiously when handled. It is not poisonous, and has only short, sharp teeth, not fangs like the Rattlesnake, but the bite of a larger Gopher Snake is enough for all but the most insistent snake collector. This snake, unfortunately, somewhat resembles the Rattlesnake in coloration and is sometimes mistaken for its poisonous relative. However, since both the Gopher Snake and the Rattlesnake are important rodent-control animals, neither should be needlessly killed. The Gopher Snake is the most common snake found in the chaparral.

Western Fence Lizard

The Western Fence Lizard (*Sceloporus occidentalis*) is a small lizard that can easily be identified by its sandy gray-brown coloration, short snout, relative short tail which breaks off readily when the animal is grabbed by that organ, and two deep blue patches that run along the underbelly. The Fence Lizard does not bite and may be handled easily by the novice. This lizard eats insects, insect larvae, and other smaller lizards.

The Northern Alligator Lizard (*Gerrhonotus coeruleus*) is found in the drier parts of the San Francisco Peninsula. Like the Fence Lizard, the Alligator Lizard is identified by its tail which is usually much longer than its body, long alligator-like snout, and a fold of skin running along both sides between the front and hind legs. These large, reddish-brown lizards can give a rather hard but harmless bite if handled, but are easily captured, being somewhat less secretive and slower of movement than the Fence Lizard.

Northern Alligator Lizard

The Western Toad (*Bufo boreas*) is the only amphibian commonly found in the chaparral except during the brief rainy periods when some salamanders may emerge. Their drier, thicker skin allows them to inhabit drier areas than the thin, wet-skinned frogs. They may be found in one's back yard at night or right after a rain. Identifying features include hind legs that are shorter than the body, while most frogs have legs that exceed the body in length. Bumps, or "warts" (they do NOT cause warts), are found on the back, and the animal tends to walk rather than hop as the frog does. Toads, like frogs, primarily eat insects, but will take nearly anything that moves if it can be forced down the throat. Toads are preyed upon by snakes, hawks, raccoons, and of course the Coyote.

Western Toad

California Newt

Birds

The most common large bird on the Peninsula is the foraging Red-tailed Hawk (*Buteo jamaicensis*). This hawk has a wing span up to three feet, and a large heavy dark body. Its long, broad, blunt-ended wings and broad tail are usually held in a horizontal position during its soaring high above the grasslands and chaparral of the Peninsula. The Red-tailed Hawk eats mice, rats, rabbits, birds, and some snakes. In view of its feeding habits it must be considered a pest control factor in our environment. All hawks are protected by law in California.

Red-tailed Hawk

The Turkey Vulture (*Cathartes aura*) can be differentiated from the Red-tailed Hawk by the position of the wings during soaring. The naked-headed vulture holds its wings above the horizontal which gives it a slight "V" appearance while soaring. It also results in a slight wobble or unsteadyness in its flight. The Turkey Vulture is a carrion eater and, along with the sea gull, helps maintain the pleasantness of our forests. The six-foot wingspan makes this bird one of the largest on the peninsula.

Turkey Vulture

The Sparrow Hawk (*Falco sparverius*) is a small falcon that is about the size of a large robin. It is also the most common hawk on the peninsula. It can be seen hovering on rapidly beating wings 15 to 30 feet over the grassy knolls nearly every clear day of the week. Its main diet is the grasshopper and other insects, but can and does occasionally take small birds such as sparrows and finches. The Sparrow

Sparrow Hawk

Great Horned Owl

White-crowned Sparrow

Golden-crowned Sparrow

Hawk is the most beautiful rapter in Northern California. Its rusty-colored back is barred with blue stripes. It has blue and orange markings on the head, and dark bluish wings. Its feathered legs are light reddish-brown.

The Great Horned Owl (*Bubo virginianus*) is the largest nocturnal predator in San Mateo County. It can usually be seen perched on telephone poles, trees, or other high places in the early evening. Its size (52" wing spread and 24" body), two "horns," or tufts of feathers on an otherwise flat head, and large bright yellow eyes distinguish this animal from other owls in the area. It feeds primarily upon rabbits, rodents, and some nocturnal birds including other smaller owls.

Perhaps the most numerous birds in the chaparral are the "dickie birds," the finches, sparrows, hummingbirds, bluebirds, chickadee, etc. Most of these are either seed eaters or insect eaters, and are very important to the ecology of that biome. We will limit our discussion to only the most obvious of these birds which the casual visitor to the chaparral will more than likely encounter. These may be classified into three main groups: seed eaters, insect eaters, and other types of feeders.

Two major seed-eating types of "dickie birds" are the finches and sparrows. These are, perhaps, the most numerous birds in the chaparral. They can most easily be identified by their flight patterns. Finches tend to undulate in flight by flapping their wings for a second or two, gaining altitude, then fold their wings along their bodies and sail ballistically up, over, and down. Then they flap again to gain altitude. The sparrows fly much more consistently. Sparrows flap continuously from take off to landing.

The White-crowned Sparrow (*Zonotrichia leucophrys*) is one of the most strikingly patterned of the sparrows. Its head has two distinct rows of black and white stripes. This sparrow is easily distinguished from the Golden-crowned Sparrow (*Zonotrichia atricapilla*) by the yellow-gold colored stripes on the latter replacing the white stripes of the former.

The Fox Sparrow (*Passerella iliaca*) is somewhat larger than the White-crowned Sparrow. Fox Sparrows grow to 6-7 inches in length. They are dark brownish-gray with heavy spotting and streaking on the breast. The back is a rusty colored brown, making it the only sparrow-like bird with this distinctly reddish-brown coloration with the exception of the English Sparrow (*Passer domesticus*) which is not a true sparrow, but belongs to the Weaver Finch family (Ploceidae).

The Song Sparrow (*Melospiza melodia*) is dark gray above and white below with stripes all over. It is the only sparrow with a distinct large black spot on its breast. This seed-eater is in greater abundance in high, or mountain chaparral and pine forests.

The California Linnet or House Finch (*Carpodacus mexicanus*) is the most common finch in San Mateo County, and is the back yard songster of the Peninsula. The male is brownish with a bright red throat and chest. Its darkly striped chest and sides may be used as identifying features. The

Fox Sparrow

English Sparrow

Song Sparrow

House Finch

Purple Finch

American Goldfinch

female House Finch is drab and sparrow-like in color. Both are about the size of a White-crowned Sparrow (5"). Finches eat, in addition to seeds, berries, thistles, fleshy plants, and other small fruit, but its conical bill identifies it as primarily a seed-eater.

The Purple Finch (*Carpodacus purpureus*) is the reddest of the finches. The male is similar to the House Finch, but lacks the dark striping. Its song is a beautiful, fast warble. Flocks of from 10 to 20 of these birds may be seen flying from bush to bush, or feeding on the ground.

The Common, or American Goldfinch (*Spinus tristis*) is a bright canary yellow with a black forehead, wings, and tail. The females are duller, and more greenish-yellow than the males. The male Green-backed Goldfinch (*Spinus psaltria*) is similar to the male Common Goldfinch but it does not have the bright yellow back. The song of this bird, like all of the finches, is a beautiful warble most noticeable in the early morning. It is not actually a "song for joy" but more of a territorial warning to other male finches that might be tempted to invade its domain.

Green-backed Goldfinch

Violet-green Swallow

Bluebird

Poorwill

Wrentit

Sage

A Check List of Chaparral Plants and Animals

Those with the asterisks are mentioned in this chapter.

Plants

* Scrub Oak (*Quercus dumosa*)
* Leather Oak (*Q. durata*)
* Interior Live Oak (*Q. wislizenii*)
* Coast Live Oak (*Q. agrifolia*)
  Oregon Oak (*Q. garryana*)
* California Laurel (*Umbellularia californica*)
* Hoary Manzanita (*Arctostaphylos canescens*)
  California Poppy (*Eschscholzia californica*)
* Chamise (*Adenostoma fasciculatum*)
* Coffeeberry (*Rhamnus californica*)
* Buck Brush (*Ceanothus cuneatus*)
* Toyon (*Photinia arbutifolia*)
* Poison Oak (*Rhus diversiloba*)
* Coyote Bush (*Baccharis pilularis*)
  California Buckwheat (*Eriogonum fasciculatum*)
  Chaparral Current (*Ribes malvaceum*)
  Gooseberry (*R. speciosum*)
  California Blackberry (*Rubus vitifolius*)
  Western Thimbleberry (*R. parviflorus*)
  Gorse (*Ulex europaeus*)
  Birch leaf Mountain Mahogany (*Cercocarpus betuloides*)
  Hollyleaf Cherry (*Prunus ilicifolia*)
  Particolor Lupine (*Lupinus variicolor*)
  California Chaparral Pea (*Pickeringia montana*)
  Squaw Bush Sumac (*Rhus trilobata*)
  Buck Thorn (*Rhamnus crocea*)
  Yerba Santa (*Eriodictyon californicum*)
* Spearmint (*Mentha spicata*)
  Spanish Bayonet (*Yucca baccata*)
  Black Sage (*Salvia mellifera*)
  Bush Monkey Flower (*Mimulus aurantiacus*)
  Common Snowberry (*Symphoricarpos albus*)
  California Sagebrush (*Artemisia californica*)
  Pacific Stonecrop (*Sedum spathulifolium*)
  Wedge-leaf Horkelia (*Horkelia cuneata*)
  Cow Parsnip (*Heracleum lanatum*)

Plants (continued)

Western Bracken Fern *(Pteridium aquilinum)*
Pine Bluegrass *(Poa scabrella)*
Wild Oat *(Avena fatua)*
Common Velvetgrass *(Holcus lanata)*
California Oatgrass *(Danthonia californica)*
Fremont's Star Lily *(Zygadenus fremontii)*
Soap Plant *(Chlorogalum pomeridianum)*
Indian Warrior *(Pedicularis densiflora)*
Scotch Broom *(Cytisus scoparius)*

Mammals

* Mule Deer *(Odocoileus hemionus)*
* Cougar *(Felis concolor)*
* Bobcat *(Lynx rufus)*
* Coyote *(Canis latrans)*
* Grey Fox *(Urocyon cinereoargenteus)*
* Beechey Ground Squirrel *(Otospermophilus beecheyi)*
Raccoon *(Procyon lotor)*
Common Opossum *(Didelphis marsupialis)*
Long-tailed Weasel *(Mustela frenata)*
Striped Skunk *(Mephitis mephitis)*
* Norway Rat *(Rattus norvegicus)*
* Wood Rat *(Neotoma fuscipes)*
* Trowbridge Shrew *(Sorex trowbridgii)*
Pocket Gopher *(Thomomys bottae)*
Deer Mouse *(Peromyscus maniculatus)*
Brush Mouse *(P. boylii)*
Pinyon Mouse *(P. truei)*
West Harvest Mouse *(Reithrodontomys megalotis)*
California Pocket Mouse *(Perognathus californicus)*
Brush Rabbit *(Sylvilagus bachmani)*
Black-tailed Jack Rabbit *(Lepus californicus)*
Bats - in - General *(Myotis spp.; Lasiurus spp.)*
Ring-tailed Cat *(Bassariscus astutus)*

CHAPARRAL

Reptiles and Amphibians

* Western Rattlesnake (*Crotalus viridis*)
* Common Kingsnake (*Lampropeltis getulus*)
* Gopher or Bull Snake (*Pituophis catenifer*)
* Western Fence Lizard (*Sceloporus occidentalis*)
* Northern Alligator Lizard (*Gerrhonotus coeruleus*)
  Western Garter Snake (*Thamnophis elegans*)
  Western Ring-necked Snake (*Diadophis amabilis*)
  Racer (*Coluber constrictor*)
* Western Skink (*Eumeces skiltonianus*)
  Eschscholtz's Salamander (*Ensatina eschscholtzi*)
  California Slender Salamander (*Batrachoseps attenuatus*)
  Arboreal Salamander (*Aneides lugubris*)
* Western Toad (*Bufo boreas*)

Birds

* Red-tailed Hawk (*Buteo jamaicensis*)
* Turkey Vulture (*Cathartes aura*)
* Sparrow Hawk (*Falco sparverius*)
* Great Horned Owl (*Bubo virginianus*)
  California Quail (*Lophortyx californicus*)
  Poor Will (*Phalaenoptilus nuttalli*)
  Anna Hummingbird (*Calypte anna*)
  Allen Hummingbird (*Selasphorus sasin*)
* White-crowned Sparrow (*Zonotrichia leucophrys*)
* Golden-crowned Sparrow (*Z. atricapilla*)
* Fox Sparrow (*Passerella iliaca*)
* English Sparrow (*Passer domesticus*)
* Song Sparrow (*Melospiza melodia*)
* Linnet or House Finch (*Carpodacus mexicanus*)
* Purple Finch (*C. purpureus*)
* American Goldfinch (*Spinus tristis*)
* Green-backed Goldfinch (*S. psaltria*)
  Ash-throated Flycatcher (*Myiarchus cinerascens*)
  Scrub Jay (*Aphelocoma coerulescens*)
  Bush Tit (*Psaltriparus minimus*)
  Wren Tit (*Chamaea fasciata*)
  Bewick Wren (*Thryomanes bewickii*)
  House Wren (*Troglodytes aedon*)
  Western Bluebird (*Sialia mexicana*)

Birds (continued)

Cedar Waxwing *(Bombycilla cedrorum)*
Gray Vireo *(Vireo vicinior)*
Tolmei Warbler *(Oporornis tolmiei)*
Pileolated Warbler *(Wilsonia pusilla)*
Spotted Towhee *(Pipilo erythrophthalmus)*
Brown Towhee *(P. fuscus)*
Lazuli Bunting *(Passerina amoena)*
Lark Sparrow *(Chondestes grammacus)*
Rufous-crowned Sparrow *(Aimophila ruficeps)*
Bell Sparrow *(Amphispiza belli)*
Black-chinned Sparrow *(Spizella atrogularis)*
Violet-green Swallow *(Tachycineta thalassina)*

Field Exercise #5

Name _____
Score _____

List the common plants endemic to the chaparral.

1.   7.   14.
2.   8.   15.
3.   9.   16.
4.   10.   17.
5.   11.   18.
6.   12.   19.
                  13.   20.

List the observed animals noted on this field trip.

Invertebrates   "Herps"   Birds   Mammals
1.   1.   1.   1.
2.   2.   2.   2.
3.   3.   3.   3.
4.   4.   4.   4.
5.   5.   5.   5.
6.   6.   6.
7.   7.   7.
8.   8.   8.
9.   9.   9.
10.   10.   10.
11.   11.
12.   12.
13.   13.
14.   14.
15.   15.

Field Exercise #6   Name_____

                                     Score_____

    Discuss the positioning of the various biomes characteristic of the Santa Cruz mountain ranges.

THE SAVANNA AND GRASSLANDS

A trip south down Skyline Boulevard to Woodside and into Portola Valley will show several of the peninsula's most beautiful biomes. You will parallel the famous San Andreas fault which runs down under the lakes. On this side of the lakes you will drive through a grassy, shrubby, tree-patched area called a savanna. The same type of biome can be found along the coast south from Half Moon Bay into Santa Cruz on the western side of the mountains and in many of the small valleys. On the other side (west) of the lakes, on the east slope of the Santa Cruz ranges, you will see the northern coastal shrub or chaparral. We will discuss the savanna or grasslands along with its plants and animals in this chapter.

As you drive south along Skyline you will note that the road is lined with several main types of trees. Some of these trees were planted as windbreaks and some are natural inhabitants of this area. The larger trees that you see will be the Monterey Pines, the Monterey Cypress and the Blue Gum, or Eucalyptus. The first two were described in the Moss Beach Chapter.

The Blue Gum (*Eucalyptus globulus*) is a tree which grows to over 150 feet and has greenish bark that becomes brownish when dry. This bark peels off very easily especially during rain or wind storms. There are two types of leaves on this tree. The main leaves are long, lance-shaped and are green. The base of the tree produces smaller, roundish and bluish leaves. The flowers are white and form small, 1 inch, nut-like fruits. All the Eucalypti are imports from Australia. When the leaves of this plant are crushed they tend to give off a strong odor resembling camphor or Vicks. There are 522 species of Eucalyptus trees growing in the world and many are imports to the Bay Area.

At the base of these large trees you will note some smaller, yellowish-leaved trees. These trees are Black Acacias (*Acacia melanoxylon*). Their leaves are smooth and have blunt ends, and are not really leaves. The real

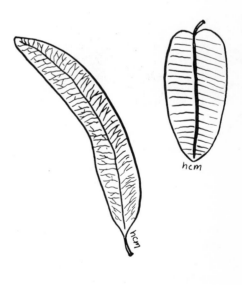

Blue Gum

131

Black Acacia

Monterey Cypress

leaves are small, dark green, and doubly compound. The leaf-like structure is really an expanded petiole that has small nondescript veins. The flowers look like small puffs of light yellow. Many other acacia trees are common to our area.

As you continue south you will note a change in the main trees. Lining the road across from the Crystal Springs Golf Course you will see hundreds of Monterey Cypress (*Cupressus macrocarpa*). These beautiful trees were planted as a windbreak. Note the small, green, overlapping, scale-like leaves, the rough bark and the rounded cones. On the sides and top of Cahill ridge directly west of the lakes you will also find this tree growing in profusion. On the west side of the road many Monterey Pines (*Pinus radiata*) have been planted. Further south you pass through another Gum grove and then the savanna becomes more obvious. The savanna from Black Mountain Road south into Portola Valley is more grass and shrubs with only patches of trees in the more protected and gullied areas.

The high afternoon temperatures, the lack of rain, the thin soil and the large amount of insolation are all restrictive factors for the plant life of this area. The afternoons are usually hot and sunny causing much evaporation. The area receives about 20 inches of rain per year but the thinness of the soil allows for only a little water to soak in. Most of the rain comes in the winter months and provides a short growing season. The soil, besides being thin, is also very rocky, not very fertile and the ground is broken by many rocks and large boulders. The gullies are protected, have more leaf litter, organics and soil, and therefore have more shrubs and trees while the open slopes are grassy and rocky.

The most obvious plants in the open savanna are the grasses. There are several hundred grasses found in the California grasslands. While only a few of the most common and important ones will be mentioned here, the grasses do serve several ecological functions. Their fibrous roots tend

to hold the soil from eroding while the root hairs along with some chemicals they produce, tend to make soil from rock. The seeds of the grasses
serve as food for many of the savanna birds and mammals. The leaves and
stems also are food for the browsing animals such as deer, rabbits, rodents,
and cattle.

There are more than 25 species of
brome grasses found in California.
The main ones in our savannas are the
Red Bromes and Soft Chess.

The Red Brome (*Bromus rubens*)
[also called Foxtail] is about 18 inches
tall and has purplish, hairy tufts on the
ends of the main stems. The main
stems are also hairy and erect. The
Red Brome is an annual with leaves that
have hairy sheaths and blades. The
Foxtail utilizes its dried, prickly seed
covering as a means of seed dispersal.
This sharp covering catches in the fur
of animals or the clothing of people and
it may be transported some distance
from the parent plant before being
pulled out and discarded on the ground.

Foxtail Brome

The Soft Chess (*Bromus hordeaceus*)
grows to about two feet in height and
is very soft and hairy. The flowers
and fruits grow on erect stems in spikelets each of which hold 7 to 9 seeds.
Ten to twenty spikelets are found on the
end of each erect stem.

Five species of wild barley are found
in California with the Mouse Barley, or
Farmer's Foxtail (*Hordeum murinum*)
being the most common. This grass
looks very similar to Red Brome grass
but the flower is not purple but whitish.
This plant is also a bit taller than the
Red Bromes.

The Wild Oats (*Avena fatua*) grow to
more than three feet tall and are some
of our most common weeds. These
annuals have leaf blades that are long,

Soft Chess

broad, and rough. The seeds grow loosely spaced on an erect stem. The seeds each have a bristle which is reddish-brown in color. The lower leaves and the seeds are edible for most animals and even for man if cooked into a mush.

The California Oat Grass (*Danthonia californica*) is a tall (about three feet), tufted perennial. It has most of the leaf blades growing very low on the plant stem. The leaves are rough and stiff. The seed-bearing stem is high and contains from 2 to 5 spikelets which hold the seeds.

Velvet Grass (*Holcus lanata*) is a perennial grass with one-to-three foot erect stems. The leaves are soft, flat blades about six inches long. The whole plant is grayish and covered with a velvety hair. The seed-producing flowers are long, narrow and tinged with purple.

Of the 15 species of needle grass found in California, *Stipa pulchia* (California Needle Grass) is the most common in the open ground of the coastal mountains. All needle grasses have spikes projecting from them which have sharp points that can stick in the skin of animals. These one-to-three foot perennials have inrolled leaves.

Other common grasses are the Fescues with 26 species, (*Poa*) the Blue Grasses with 29 species, and the Rye Grasses (*Lolium*) with 3 common types. See the reference books for the descriptions of these and the hundreds of other grasses.

Besides the grasses, thistles and teasels are very common in this area. There is only one main teasel in our

Farmer's Foxtail

Wild Oats

grasslands. The Fuller's Teasel (*Dip-sacus Fullonum*) is a weed that is a stout, prickly, biennial herb. This plant grows to a height of three to six feet and has large leaves that are ob-long, broad and somewhat sickle-shaped. The teasel has pinkish-white flowers formed into a dense head which when dry forms a prickly, pointed, oblong spike. This spike has four main long spikes projecting from the main head. The bracts or small projections coming out of the head are curved into hooks. This weed like many others is an import from Europe.

The most common thistles in our county are: the Napa Thistles, Indian Thistles, and the Purple and Yellow Star Thistles.

The one-to-two foot Napa Thistle (*Centaurea melitensis*) can easily be identified by the leaves which hug the stem, partially surrounding them. The leaves then come out forming a wing-like structure. The lower leaves are larger and cleft while the upper leaves are smaller, narrow and not cleft. The spikes of the flower are globular, yel-low and about one-half an inch high. These spikes are sometimes found in groups of two or three.

The Indian Thistle (*Cirsium edule*), a biennial, is a native thistle in the Bay Area and it grows to six feet in height. The leaves are thin, indented and about eight inches long with many prickly spines growing over the surface. The leaves are whitish and hairy beneath but are dark green above. The flowers vary from white to pink or purple. This plant is edible if picked when very young and cooked.

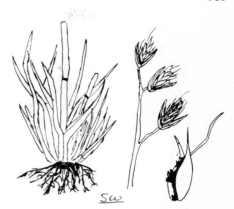

California Oat Grass

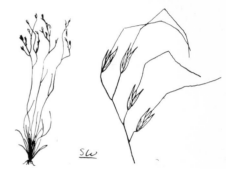

Needlegrass

Fuller's Teasel

Indian Thistle

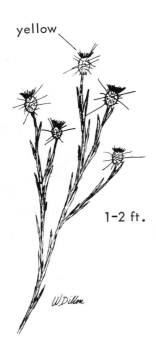

yellow

1-2 ft.

W Dillon

Yellow Star Thistle

The Purple Star Thistle (*Centaurec
calcitrapa*) is very common in Sar
Mateo County along the roads. It grows
to four feet in height and is a perennial
The young stems and leaves are covered
with a cobweb-like hair. The narrow
segmented leaves have small clear pits
or globules on their upper surface. The
flowers are purple, one-half to one inch
long and have straw-colored spines and
prickles projecting from them. A close
relative also found here is the Yellow
Star Thistle (*C. solstitialis*). This
plant is very similar to its purple cousin but is shorter, (one to two feet). I
has bright yellow flowers with small
leaves similar to the Napa Thistle
The flowers of the thistles serve a
food for many grazing animals as wel
as the hummingbirds which feed on th
nectar and the water trapped amon
the petals. Sparrows and finches ea
the seeds from the mature, dry frui

Many flowers, shrubs, and som
trees grow in the San Mateo grassland
depending upon the environmental fac
tors, the slope of the land and the dept
of the soil.

The main trees found in our grass
areas are the Coast Live Oaks, the Ba
Laurels, the California Buckeyes an
a few misplaced Blue Gum trees. W
have also described most of these tree
in other chapters.

The Coast Live Oaks (*Quercus agri
folia*) in the savanna are found near th
roads and in any stream-like depres
sions or gullies leading from the top
of ridges. This tree has a dark, smoot
bark on the trunk and limbs. Th
leaves are holly-like, shiny and gree
on both sides. The upper side is darke

and the margins of the leaves have reg-
ularly spaced spines. The leaf is bowed
or humped. The acorn is slender,
pointed and about 1 to 1 1/2 inches long
with five to seven vertical lines running
the length of the acorn. The Acorn
Woodpecker (*Melanerpes formicivorus*)
can often be seen perched on the trunk
feeding on insects which live under the
bark of the tree. Other birds which
feed in the grasslands may seek refuge
in the oak trees.

Coast Live Oak

There are some California Laurels
(*Umbellularia californica*) in our savanna. This tree varies in height depending upon the amount of water and
depth of soil. The laurel has evergreen
leaves that are dark, shiny green above
and dull-colored below. The flowers
bloom in the winter, look like a yellow
puff and they ripen into an olive-like
fruit. The leaves have a good-smelling
odor when dry and they can be used to
season soups and other foods. Very
few other plants can grow under the
laurel because of the oily secretions
deposited on the soil by the fallen leaves.
This tree is the last member of the
genus Umbellularia, that was widespread throughout the West during the
Pliocene epoch. This tree is now fairly
restricted to Oregon and California.

Many shrubs are found along the
roads and in the fields of the savanna.
Some are natives to this area but many
have been introduced through the efforts
of man or by accident.

The most common shrub in our savanna and in the entire county is the
Coyote Bush (*Baccharis pilularis*) which
is a shrubby plant that grows to more
than five feet in height. The leaves are

Red-head Woodpecker

small, about 1/4 inch wide and about one inch long, and are greenish-yellow in color. When in flower the ends of the branches are covered with small whitish flowers, in vase-shaped pods. The stems appear dry and gray and the leaves are found only on the outermost portions of the stem.

Another common shrub in the savanna is the Toyon or Christmas Berry (*Photinia arbutifolia*). This plant is easily identified by the dark green, toothed leaves and the bright red fruits. These red fruits form in the fall after the small white flowers disappear. The fruits are edible and provide food for birds and small mammals.

Yellow and blue lupins (*Lupinus spp.*) are common along Skyline and other roads in the county. These plants become very common further south near

Bay Laurel

Coyote Bush

Toyon

Woodside and also along the coast in grassy areas. The coastal lupins may also be of the white variety. The lupins have greenish leaves with palmate arrangement. The flowers change in the fall to a bean-like pod that rattles when dry and the seeds provide food for small animals. The seeds are dark brown and round.

Along the roads and in patches in the gullies we find the infamous Poison Oak (*Rhus diversiloba*). This plant can be found either as a bush or climbing vine. The leaf is divided into three leaflets and these leaflets are reddish-green in color when new. They turn green in the summer and then change to red again in the fall. The leaves fall off the plant during the winter. The plant has greenish flowers and white berry-like fruits. The leaves produce

Yellow Lupine

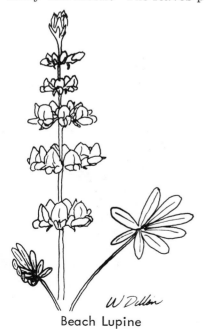

Beach Lupine

Poison Oak

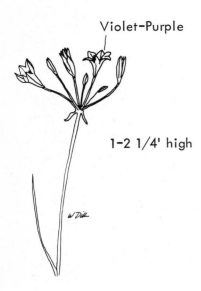

Violet-Purple

1-2 1/4' high

Grass Nut

an oil which may cause blisters and other irritations to the skin.

Many flowers and weeds are common along the roads, in patches near rocks or in the open grassy areas. It is impossible to mention all of them, so only the most common and obvious ones will be noted.

The Grass Nut (*Brodiaea laxa*) and the Bluedicks (*Brodiaea capitata*) have lily-like flowers and they grow along the roads such as Sawyer Camp Road and in the adjoining fields from bulbs. Both have grass-like leaves. The Grass Nut has a flower head with up to 48 flowers. Each flower is about one inch long and is violet or purple. Bluedicks are about the same height as Grass Nut, two feet, but they have only 8 to 10 blue-lavender flowers in a close cluster.

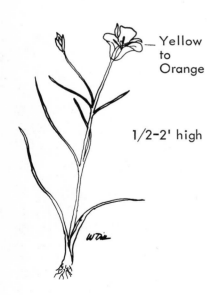

Yellow
to
Orange

1/2-2' high

Yellow Mariposa

California Poppy

The Yellow Mariposa (*Calochortus luteus*) is the most common lily-type flower in our savanna but other mariposa-type flowers may be found. It has orange-yellow flowers which may have brown markings. The flower stem comes out of a small roundish bulb. This plant grows to over two feet and the long narrow leaves grow from the slender stem.

The California Golden Poppy (*Eschscholzia californica*) is our state flower and is found in abundance throughout the county. The orange-gold color adds to the beauty of our countryside. The flower is poppy-like with four broad petals and may vary from pure orange to white but it is usually orange. The flowers curl into a tight cone when the temperature drops and when the sun goes down, only to reopen the following

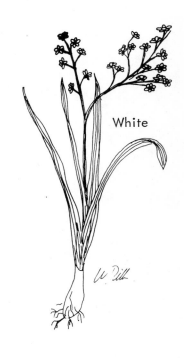

White

Star Lily

Butter Cup

Blue-eyed Grass

morning. The leaves are branched into segments and are light green. After flowering a long, pointed fruit pod with brown seeds is formed. The dry seeds fall and reseed the plant each year. California was named the "Golden State" because the hills were covered with millions of these beautiful flowers and not because of the discovery of gold.

Many common grassland weeds and flowers are already familiar to most people. We will list some of these and then describe others in more detail. You should know by sight the Butter Cup, Bur and Sweet Clover, Golden Rod, Yarrow, Wild Asters and some of the weeds like the Mustards and Radishes.

Miner's Lettuce (*Montia perfoliata*) is one of the less obvious of plants. The plant grows from about eight to

Yarrow

Douglas Iris

Yellow

Gold Fields

twelve inches tall, is a nice green col-
or, and has tiny white flowers. The
one inch leaves are roundish and the
flowers seem to grow out of the center
of the basal leaves. This is another
of our many edible plants. The leaves
are good in salads or eaten alone. The
California Indians used to take the
Miner's Lettuce leaves and put them
near ant hills. The ants in moving
across the leaves would leave secretions of acetic acid. These secretions
taste like vinegar.

The Monkey Flower (*Mimulus guttatus*) is a two-foot plant with a single
stem. Some Monkey Flowers are
orange, yellow or red and they have
purple or brown dots down inside the
opening of the flower. The flower looks
comically somewhat like a face. The
leaves look like a fan with the veins

Miner's Lettuce

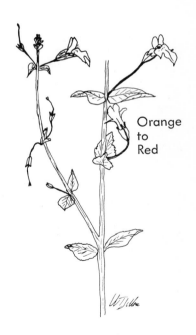

Orange
to
Red

Henderson's Shooting Star

Monkey Flower

Sticky Monkey

all coming out from a single point. (See appendix of palmate venation.)

Another similar flower often confused with the Monkey Flower is the "Sticky Monkey" or Bush Monkey Flower (*Diplacus aurantiacus*). The Sticky Monkey has more narrow leaves and has pinnate venation. The leaves feel very sticky. This plant is very common along roads and in the chaparral.

Two plants very common along the roads in our county and in open fields are the Common Parsnip (Cow Parsnip) and the Poison Hemlock. The dry stalks and flowers look similar but the leaves are quite different.

The Cow Parsnip (*Heracleum lanatum*) grows to more than six feet, has a broad green leaf divided into three large leaf-like lobes. Each leaf is about three to six inches across. The

Cow Parsnip

Poison Hemlock

flowers are white and candelabra-shaped, are small and arranged in a bouquet-like inflorescence. The flowers produce many large, round, flat seeds.

The Poison Hemlock (*Conium maculatum*) however, grows taller, up to ten feet, but the flowers are similar. The leaves are quite different. Each leaf is divided into three sub-branches, each sub-branch with smaller sub-branches. This plant is poisonous if eaten, while parsnips' stems are very edible.

The Scarlet Pimpernel (*Anagillis arvensis*) is a low vine-like weed that grows about two feet long if in a moist area. It is much shorter in dry soil. The stems hug the ground, have opposite leaves and scarlet to orange flowers. The flowers open each day and close at night. These flowers form small round seed pods that look like small balls on a dry string.

Red Stem Filaree

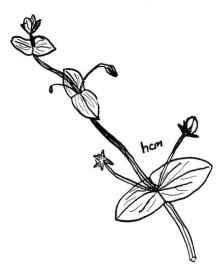

Scarlet Pimpernel

These few plants mentioned are by no means the only ones to be found in the grasslands. Also many plants, trees, flowers and weeds can be found in our peninsula's savannas that have been imported or have escaped from farms and gardens in this area. The hundreds of spring and fall wild flowers which abound in our savannas are too numerous and too ephemeral to be mentioned individually. Please note the reference books for more information on these beautiful and interesting plants.

The animals found in the local savannas are extremely interesting and of two main types. The two types are the animals that normally live in this area and the animals that pass through this area in daily or seasonal migration. Many chaparral and domestic plants and animals can be found in these grassy areas.

The main native animals in the savanna are either diurnal (day active) or nocturnal (night active). The majority of the larger animals are only seen at night. The primary animals seen in the savanna during the day are the birds, rodents, insects, and reptiles. These animals feed upon grasses, shrubs, carrion, insects and the other animals found in the area.

Turkey Vulture

The most obvious animals seen in the day in the grassy areas are birds like the vultures, hawks, and song birds.

The Turkey Vulture (*Cathartes aura*) is the largest bird seen in our area. It has a wingspan of more than 6', has black feathers except on the outer edges of its underwing where the feathers are gray. The Turkey Vulture has a red, naked neck and head. These larger birds feed primarily on carrion or dead animals found in the grasslands or alongside the roads. A large flock of about 50 Turkey Vultures nest in 2 groups of Eucalyptus trees north of Hilldale and Skyline Road in Millbrae. The birds build nests in the trees by dropping dry sticks into the crotches of tree limbs.

Three hawks are commonly found in our grasslands. The three are the Red-tailed Hawk, the Sparrow Hawk and the Swainson's Hawk. All are carnivorous and eat small mammals, birds, reptiles, and insects. Of the three, the Sparrow Hawk eats more insect life and small birds than do the other two.

The Sparrow Hawk (*Falco sparverius*) is a small falcon that is about the size of a large robin. It is also about the most common small hawk-like bird in the San Mateo County. The Sparrow Hawk can be seen hovering, on rapidly beating wings, over grassy knolls nearly every clear day. Its small size, its blue and orange head markings, its bluish wings, and reddish-brown back feathers are its main characteristics. This bird often rests on telephone wires, or fences surveying its domain. Its call is a sharp and rapid "Killy-Killy-Killy." Its main diet is the grasshoppers and the other insects (69%), but it can and does occasionally take small birds (8%) such as sparrows and finches, and about 19% rodents.

The most common large bird in San Mateo County is the foraging Red-tailed Hawk (*Buteo jamaicensis*). This hawk has a wingspan of up to three feet and a large, heavy, dark body. The feathers are darker above and lighter on the breast and belly. The tail feathers are bright red on the upper surface. Its relatively short, broad wings and tail are usually held in a horizontal position during its soaring high above the grasslands and forests of the peninsula. In view of its feeding habits it must be considered a pest-control factor in our environment. In feeding it will soar for long periods and then suddenly dive on its prey and capture the smaller food animal in its talons. This hawk also eats an occasional game bird or

LAWRENCE
CARSON

Sparrow Hawk

LAWRENCE
CARSON

Red-tailed Hawk

chicken, but it should not be considered a "Chicken Hawk." The Red-tailed Hawk eats primarily mice and rats (55%), rabbits, birds, and some snakes.

The last hawk to be mentioned in this discussion of the savanna is the Swainson's Hawk (*Buteo swainsoni*). This bird is uniformly dark on top. When seen from below, the wings appear two-toned with the inner portions lighter or white, while the outer feathers are dark. The breast and belly are gray. The tail feathers have a marked banding with the widest, darkest bands near the tip. The tip of the tail itself, however, is edged with light gray. The Swainson's Hawk is about the size of a Red-tailed Hawk (19-22"), but may appear somewhat slimmer. This bird also flies with a slight vulture-like dihedral to its wings. A prime pest-control factor in our environment, the Swainson's Hawk's diet consists of about 50% rodents, 30% insects, and 20% snakes and other animals.

In San Mateo County the savanna is near and paralleling a series of man-made lakes—Lake San Andreas and the Crystal Springs Reservoir. Many birds commonly seen at Moss Beach or along the bay shores and in the salt marshes will be seen resting or feeding in the lakes. For the descriptions of the gulls, ducks, and other water birds please turn to the appropriate chapters. Other large birds common to the savannas are the crows and ravens. The Raven (*Corvus corax*) is the larger of the two. It is pure black and has spine-like feathers projecting from his throat area. The Crow (*Corvus brachyrhynchos*) is slightly smaller, about 18"

Goshawk

Swainson's Hawk

long and is also black, but it has smooth
throat feathers. The raven croaks
"Krruach" while the crow calls "caw-
caw-caw-caw-caw." Both are carrion
eaters, or scavengers, but will also
eat insects and other small animals,
dead or alive.

Raven

Another all black, robin-sized bird
common to our savannas is the Brewer's
Blackbird (*Euphagus cyanocephalus*).
The males can be easily distinguished
from the females. The male is pure
black with a white eye while the female
is grayish and has dark eyes. These
are seed and insect eaters, commonly
occurring in large flocks. These birds
tend to be very aggressive during the
breeding season. They will defend
their nest by swooping down upon intruders and even attacking them. They
have been seen attacking hawks, cats,
and even the observer.

Crow

One of the most beautiful birds found
in the grasslands is our "state bird,"
the California Quail (*Lophortyx californicus*). These small 10" birds are
plump, chicken-like and both sexes
have a short head plume that curves
forward. The male has a more distinctive black and white pattern on its
face. These birds also live in social
flocks for their mutual protection.
They feed upon seeds and insects. The
quail usually frequent favored "dusting"
areas for "bathing" purposes. Quail
roost in trees at night, but build their
nests on the ground.

Brewer's Blackbird

Two kingbirds are found in the
grasslands. They are the Western
Kingbird (*Tyrannus verticalis*) and
Cassin's Kingbird (*T. vociferans*).
Both are robin-sized and are similar

California Quail

in coloration, having gray heads and backs, with yellowish or white chest and belly feathers and black tail feathers. The Western Kingbird has a white margin on its tail feathers. Kingbirds are fly catchers and they sit on exposed perches waiting for flying insects which they chase and capture. They often return to the same perch. Kingbirds may also feed on ground-living insects like grasshoppers.

A small bird and predator found in several biomes is the Loggerhead Shrike (*Lanius ludovicianus*). The shrike is smaller than a robin, steel gray above, white below and has black markings through the eye, on the wing tips and tail. This bird will capture many insects, small rodents, and small reptiles and will hang its victim's body on sharp branches or barbed wire fences.

Western Kingbird

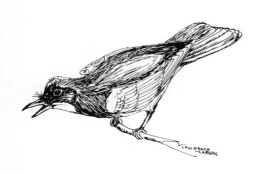

Cassin's Kingbird

Shrike

There are 2 "hummers" common to
our grassy areas. The Anna's Hummingbird (*Calypte anna*) and Allen's
Hummingbird (*Selasphorus sasin*) are
both nectar feeders, acquiring their
food from grassland and chaparral
flowers. These are the two primary
hummingbirds of the Bay Area back
yards. Their nests are small hanging
basket-like structures, with only a
small opening in the top. The male of
each species is brighter in color while
the females are drab green. The male
Anna's Hummingbird is about 3" long
with a red forehead and throat while
the Allen's Hummingbird is smaller
and has a red throat only. The Anna's
Hummingbird does a vertical mating
"dance" flight during the courtship.
The bird climbs to an altitude of about

Allen's Hummingbird

Bullock's Oriole

Anna's Hummingbird

Western Bluebird

30 feet and then suddenly dives to within 5 feet of the ground, pulling up rapidly and emitting a sharp snap-like sound. Hummers will also defend their territory ferociously, driving out larger birds many times their own size.

Many other birds are common to the savannas. Birds such as finches, linnets, sparrows, and jays are often found feeding in the open areas. These birds have been discussed in the section on the Chaparral or will be covered elsewhere.

Amphibians and Reptiles

Chaparral Thrasher

There are few amphibians found in this peninsula's grasslands. The reptiles will be more numerous, because they require less moisture than the amphibians. Almost every lizard and snake common in our chaparral will also occur in the grassy areas—the Fence Lizards, Northern and Southern Alligator Lizards, etc. All of these animals eat insects or other small amphibians, reptiles or mammals. Only the most obvious ones will be discussed here.

Western Toad

Western Toads (*Bufo boreas*) inhabit moist, but not necessarily wet areas of the grasslands. They may be found in one's yard at night or right after a rain. Identifying features include hind legs which are about the length of the front legs. This animal tends to walk rather than hop as does the frog. Toads have bumps or warts on their back which do NOT cause warts. These warts secrete a bitter-tasting, milky fluid when disturbed. The naturalist should wash his hands after handling

this animal because the fluid can cause
a painful burning if it comes in contact
with the eyes.

The Western Rattlesnake (*Crotalus
viridis*) is the only poisonous snake
on the San Francisco Peninsula. It
seldom reaches a length of over four
feet, and is secretive and elusive. It
ranges in color from light green to
light tan, with a darker, box-like pattern of diamonds along the back. The
spade-shaped head and terminal rattles
are foolproof identifying features. The
poison injected by the bite of a rattlesnake acts primarily upon the blood
cells of the victim resulting in some
pain, swelling and usually shock of
varying degree. Research tends to indicate that the "cut and suck" treatment
for rattlesnake bite is of little help to
the victim. Cold compresses or ice
packs, and anti-venom is apparently
most effective.

The Western Rattlesnake, while of
no great danger to man, acts as another
important check on the rodent population in this area. Rattlesnakes are
numerous particularly in the dry,
grassy areas. They give birth to their
young rather than laying eggs, and the
newly-born rattlesnake is capable of
striking and injecting venom. Oddly
enough, the rattlesnake is not immune
to its own poison!

The Common Kingsnake (*Lampropeltis getulus*) is best known for its attacks on the rattlesnake. Rattlesnakes
apparently recognize the kingsnake,
and attempt every possible means of
escape. The kingsnake is immune to
the venom of the rattlesnake and usually responds aggressively in the

Rattlesnake

Kingsnake

presence of the poisonous snake. The kingsnake is a constrictor, and kills its prey by grasping it by the neck and squeezing it to death. Some records indicate that the kingsnake can swallow other snakes whole even though the victim exceeds the kingsnake in length. This snake grows to about 4' in length and is colored with alternating black and yellowish-white bands.

The Gopher Snake (*Pituophis cate-nifer*), as the name implies, eats gophers, mice, rats, moles, and other small mammals. It is another constrictor and kills its prey by coiling around it and squeezing. The Gopher Snake is yellowish-brown with black blotches. This snake often exceeds 5' in length. The Gopher Snake feeds primarily upon gophers and chases them through their tunnels. This presents a problem for in the tunnel they are unable to "constrict" in the normal manner. To kill a gopher they chase it down a tunnel and crawl between the legs and under the belly. When they are under their prey they "push" the gopher toward one side or the top of the tunnel. This in effect "constricts" the mammal until it suffocates. The gopher is then swallowed whole.

Gopher Snake

The Racers (*Coluber constrictor*) are fast-moving snakes and are some of the most voracious hunters in the grasslands. Racers grow to more than 4 feet and have a narrow, uniformly brown or bluish body. This snake is lighter in color on its ventral surface. Racers can be found foraging during the day for toads, lizards and other small animals hidden in the grass and leaf litter. As their name indicates they too are constrictors.

Racer

The Western Ring-necked Snake
(*Diadophis amabilis*) is a small and
beautifully colored snake. This animal is very secretive. It grows to
about 18 inches and is grayish on its
dorsal surface. There is an orange or
reddish-yellow ring around its neck and
the ventral surface is usually bright
red-orange. Ring-necks hide during
the day under rocks and other debris
and hunt insects, snails and small amphibians and lizards after dark.

Ring-necked Snake

The Western Fence Lizard (*Sceloporus occidentalis*) is a small lizard
which can easily be identified by its
short snout, relatively short tail, which
breaks off readily when the animal is
grabbed by that organ, and by two deep
blue patches running along the underbelly. The Fence Lizard does not bite
and is handled easily by the novice.
Like all lizards, the Fence Lizard eats
insects, grubs, and even smaller lizards. They will often eat their own off-
spring.

Fence Lizard

Both the Northern Alligator Lizard
(*Gerrhonotus coeruleus*) and the Southern or Foothill Alligator Lizard (*G.
multicarinatus*) are found on the peninsula. The northern species is yellowish and black while its close relative
is more reddish with black markings.
Like the Fence Lizard, the Alligator
Lizards eat insects, spiders, scor-
pions, etc. For this reason, they are
important as pest-control agents. The
Alligator Lizard is identified by its
long tail, long alligator-like snout, and
it has a fold of skin running along both
sides between the front and hind legs.
These lizards can give a rather hard
and painful bite if handled, but are

Alligator Lizard

Black-tail Deer

Bobcat

easily captured being somewhat less secretive and slower than the Fence Lizard.

Several mammals come into the grassy areas to feed, generally at night. Raccoon, opossum, foxes, deer, skunks, and other forest and chaparral mammals may be seen under the proper conditions. Be sure to know what animals from adjoining biomes will most likely be encountered.

The Mule Deer and the Black-tailed Deer belong to the same species (*Odocoileus hemionus*) but different subspecies. They may interbreed where their ranges overlap. Mule Deer are generally larger, heavier, and have a black tip on the tail. The Black-tailed Deer's tail is entirely black. They are very wary animals that depend upon speed and agility to escape their enemies. The antlers are shed each year in the late winter, but grow back even larger by early summer. The new antlers are soft and are covered by a velvety hair. As the antlers harden this "velvet" is rubbed off against trees and shrubs and by the late fall "rutting season", they are primed for combat. Generally, only one spotted fawn is born each year around the middle of June.

The Bobcat (*Lynx rufus*) derives its major source of food from the rodent family; however, it will eat small birds such as quail. This selection of food makes the bobcat an important factor in the ecological picture of the peninsula. While the bobcat is seldom seen, it is frequently heard "yelling" or "howling" from cover. The tufted ears, short stump of a tail, and long legs distinguish this cat from any others.

The Coyote (*Canis latrans*) is a member of the dog family, and is another important pest-control factor in our environment. The dark-tipped tail is usually carried down between the hind legs, as the coyote lopes through the grasslands. Unlike the cougar and bobcat which seem to prefer the forested areas, the coyote prefers the open, grassy areas. They make their "den" either by excavation or by taking over a hollow log.

The Grey Fox (*Urocyon cinereoargenteus*) is another member of the dog family that frequents the grasslands usually at night hunting for rodents. This animal seldom exceeds 2 feet in length. It is reddish-grey in color with a dark stripe down the back.

The remaining mammals to be discussed are rabbits, rodents and other small mammals that are grassland residents or are neighboring biome invaders that come into the grassy areas to hunt or look for food.

The grassland rabbits are of two types. The largest is the Black-tailed Jack Rabbit (*Lepus californicus*). The Jack Rabbit grows to the size of a small dog or large cat. It is characterized by the large, long, black-tipped ears and their long legs and large feet. This herbivore does not dig holes as most rabbits do, but makes a "set" or nest-like area in thick brush or near a rock or log. The animal protects itself by camouflage and speed.

The Audubon Cottontail (*Sylvilagus audibonii*) is a smaller rabbit. It is a brown-black rabbit with a white belly,

Coyote

Red Fox

Grey Fox

Jack Rabbit

Cotton-tail

Broad-handed Mole

and black-tipped ears. These white parts flash as the animal runs. This rabbit digs a hole from which it emerges at dawn and dusk to feed on soft grasses and other plant life.

Some small grassland mammals are the moles, gophers, and mice. These are also the most common of the animals found in grassy areas even if they are usually unobserved, because they are fossorial (live underground) and nocturnal (active at night).

The Broad-handed Mole (*Scapanus latimanus*) is common in the more moist areas of the savanna where the soil is suitable for their burrows and where worms and insect larvae are abundant. The mole has beautiful brown to black velvety fur and this short dense fur may appear silvery. The short hairless tail and the broad fleshy front feet are other major features. The 5-8 inch moles have small eyes and a long nose, but no visible ears. Moles make mounds near the surface as they move through the soft earth feeding. Few animals feed upon moles due to their secretive nature and the unpleasant taste of their flesh.

The Botta Pocket Gopher (*Thomomys bottae*) is an industrious and destructive rodent, much resembling the mole in behavior. The gopher is a herbivore eating the roots and stems of many plants. It gets its food and protection by digging a burrow much like that of the mole, but unlike the mole there is no surface mound. The only visible dirt moved is near the opening of its tunnel.

Gophers are rat-sized, 5-10 inches, brownish in color above and lighter on the belly and undersurface. The Pocket Gopher has a short tail, long sharp incisors and sharp claws. It gets its name from the deep, fur-lined cheek pouches. The gopher may carry food and/or nesting materials in these pouches. They also have sensitive vibrissae or whiskers used as sense organs when in their tunnels. The gophers are very fecundent animals and their high birth rate is kept under control by Gopher Snakes and rattlesnakes, hawks, weasels, and many other predators.

Pocket Gopher

Another secretive and interesting rodent found in our area is the California Meadow Mouse or Vole (*Microtus californicus*). The vole is dark brown above and light brown to white on its undersurface. They grow to 6-7 inches and have a blunt face and short tail. The tail is about 1/3 the body length and, like the body, is brown above and lighter below. The vole is a grass-eating rodent which makes tunnels in the grassy areas by eating the plants near the ground forming path-like "runs" and letting other grasses form a cover. Voles also eat seeds and grain. Voles in turn provide food for most predators including owls, weasels, and snakes. The voles are active both day and night, unlike many other rodents which may be active either day or night.

California Meadow Mouse

The last rodents to be mentioned for the savannas are the Western Harvest Mouse and the White-footed Deer Mouse, both of which are primarily nocturnal. Because of their shyness and nocturnal activity they are rarely seen even though the Deer Mouse is

Harvest Mouse

White-footed Deer Mouse

the most common and widespread rodent in the state.

The Western Harvest Mouse (*Reithrodontomys megalotis*) is a small (about 4–5 inches) mouse that has reddish to black fur on its back and sides. Like most rodents it gradually changes to white or light tan on its underside. This pretty little mouse has a well-proportioned body and a tail about 1/2 its body length. They eat primarily grasses and seeds, but will take fruits and berries. The Harvest Mouse lives in tall grass or weeds often using a bird nest as its home or they build a "ball" of grass and twigs in weeds near the ground. The nest is often lined with soft paper, or cloth or materials from trees.

Like most rodents these mice are preyed upon by many owls, hawks, snakes, foxes, skunks and other mammals like the coyote.

The White-footed Deer Mouse (*Peromyscus maniculatus*) is easily identified by its large deer-like ears, its white feet, belly, and chest and its long scaly tail, about 1/2 to 2/3 its body length. The back fur is brown or gray and the color on the sides and undersurface changes abruptly, not gradually as in most mice. This rodent is found in almost every land biome where it builds its nest under logs, in rocks or even in caves. The nest is usually a ball of twigs and grasses lined on the inside with soft, downy materials.

The Deer Mice are seed eaters, but they often include acorns, berries, insects, and almost any other food in their diet. They may store much food in their den for "hard times" or for later periods of feeding.

Other rodents and small mammals can be found locally in the San Mateo savannas. Please see the check list and references for more details.

A Check List of Savanna and Grassland
Plants and Animals

Those with the asterisks are mentioned in this chapter.

Plants

*   Coast Live Oak (*Quercus agrifolia*)
*   Blue Gum (*Eucalyptus globulus*)
*   Black Acacia (*Acacia melanoxylon*)
*   Monterey Cypress (*Cupressus macrocarpa*)
*   Monterey Pine (*Pinus radiata*)
*   Red Brome (*Bromus rubens*)
*   Soft Chess (*B. hordeaceus*)
*   Mouse Barley (*Hordeum murinum*)
*   Wild Oats (*Avena fatua*)
*   California Oat Grass (*Danthonia californica*)
*   Velvet Grass (*Holcus lanata*)
*   California Needlegrass (*Stipa pulchia*)
   Pine Bluegrass (*Poa scabrella*)
   San Francisco Bluegrass (*P. unilateralis*)
   Western Melica (*Melica californica*)
   Six-weeks Fescue (*Festuca megalura*)
   Quaking Grass (*Brazia major*)
*   Rye Grasses (*Lolium spp.*)
*   Fuller's Teasel (*Dipsacus Fullonum*)
*   Napa Thistle (*Centaurea melitensis*)
*   Purple Star Thistle (*C. calcitrapa*)
*   Yellow Star Thistle (*C. solstitialis*)
*   Indian Thistle (*Cirsium edule*)
   California Buckeye (*Aesculus californica*)
*   California Laurel (*Umbellularia californica*)
*   Coyote Bush (*Baccharis pilularis*)
*   Toyon (*Photinia arbutifolia*)
*   Poison Oak (*Rhus diversiloba*)
*   Grass Nut (*Brodiaea laxa*)
*   Bluedicks (*B. capitata*)
   Woolly Sedge (*Carex lanuginosa*)
   Blue-eyed Grass (*Sisyrinchium bellum*)
*   Yellow Mariposa (*Calochortus luteus*)
*   California Poppy (*Eschscholzia californica*)
*   Miner's Lettuce (*Montia perfoliata*)

Plants (continued)

* Monkey Flower (*Mimulus guttatus*)
* Sticky Monkey (*Diplacus aurantiacus*)
* Cow Parsnip (*Heracleum lanatum*)
* Poison Hemlock (*Conium maculatum*)
* Scarlet Pimpernel (*Anagillis arvensis*)
  Nettleleaf Goosefoot (*Chenopodium murale*)
  Mouse-Ear Chickweed (*Cerastium viscosum*)
  California Buttercup (*Ranunculus californicus*)
  Milk Maids (*Dentaria californica*)
  White-Stem Filaree (*Erodium moschatum*)
  Red-Stem Filaree (*E. cicutarium*)
  Yellow Mustard (*Brassica campestris*)
  Black Mustard (*B. nigra*)
  Hedge Mustard (*Sisymbrium officinale*)
  Shepherd's Purse (*Capsella bursa-pastoris*)
  Henderson's Shooting Star (*Dodecatheon hendersonii*)
  Milkweed (*Asclepias fascicularis*)
  Baby Blue Eyes (*Nemophila Menziesii*)
  Pacific Aster (*Aster chilensis*)
  Goldfields (*Baeria chrysostoma*)
  Escobita Owl Clover (*Orthocarpus purpurascens*)
  Wooly Painted Cup (*Castilleja foliolosa*)
  Common Madia (*Madia elegans*)
  Pearly Everlasting Flower (*Anaphalis margaritacea*)
  Tidy Tips (*Layia platyglossa*)
  Sweet Fennel (*Foeniculum vulgare*)
  Common Yarrow (*Achillea millefolium*)
  Pampas Grass (*Cortaderia selloana*)
  Big Quaking Grass (*Briza maxima*)
  Little Quaking Grass (*B. minor*)
  Ripgut Grass (*Bromus rigidus*)
  Douglas Iris (*Iris douglasiana*)

Birds

* Turkey Vulture (*Cathartes aura*)
* Sparrow Hawk (*Falco sparverius*)
* Red-tailed Hawk (*Buteo jamaicensis*)
* Swainson's Hawk (*B. swainsoni*)
  Barn Owl (*Tyto alba*)

Birds (continued)

    Great Horned Owl (*Bubo virginianus*)
    Burrowing Owl (*Speotyto cunicularia*)
    Short-eared Owl (*Asio flammeus*)
* Raven (*Corvus corax*)
* Crow (*C. brachyrhynchos*)
* Brewer's Blackbird (*Euphagus cyanocephalus*)
    Night Hawk (*Chordeiles acutipennis*)
* California Quail (*Lophortyx californicus*)
    Barn Swallow (*Hirundo rustica*)
    Cliff Swallow (*Petrochelidon phrrhonota*)
    Bank Swallow (*Riparia riparia*)
    Say Phoebe (*Sayornis saya*)
* Western King Bird (*Tyrannus verticalis*)
* Cassin's King Bird (*T. vociferans*)
    Robin (*Turdus migratorius*)
* Loggerhead Shrike (*Lanius ludovicianus*)
    Western Blue Bird (*Sialia mexicana*)
    Pipit (*Anthus spinoletta*)
    Red-winged Blackbird (*Agelaius phoeniceus*)
    Tricolored Blackbird (*A. tricolor*)
    Western Meadowlark (*Sturnella neglecta*)
    Cowbird (*Molothrus ater*)
    Bullock Oriole (*Icterus bullockii*)
    Green-backed Goldfinch (*Spinus psaltria*)
    American Goldfinch (*S. tristis*)
    Pine Suskin (*S. pinus*)
    Lincoln Sparrow (*Melospiza lincolnii*)
    Lark Sparrow (*Chondestes grammacus*)
    Western Grasshopper Sparrow (*Ammodramus savannarum*)
    English Sparrow (*Passer domesticus*)
    Rufous-Crowned Sparrow (*Aimophila ruficeps*)
* Anna's Hummingbird (*Calypte anna*)
* Allen's Hummingbird (*Selasphorus sasin*)

Amphibians and Reptiles

    Tiger Salamander (*Ambystoma tigrinum*)
    Rough-skinned Newt (*Taricha granulosa*)
    Western Spadefoot Toad (*Scaphiopus hammondi*)
* Western Toad (*Bufo boreas*)

Amphibians and Reptiles (continued)

    Red-legged Frog (*Rana aurora*)
    Yellow-legged Frog (*R. boylei*)
* Western Rattlesnake (*Crotalus viridis*)
* Common Kingsnake (*Lampropeltis getulus*)
* Gopher Snake (*Pituophis catenifer*)
* Racer (*Coluber constrictor*)
* Western Ring-neck Snake (*Diadophis amabilis*)
    Common Garter Snake (*Thamnophis sirtalis*)
    Western Garter Snake (*T. elegans*)
    Western Skink (*Eumeces skiltonianus*)
* Western Fence Lizard (*Sceloporus occidentalis*)
* Northern Alligator Lizard (*Gerrhonotus coeruleus*)
* Southern or Foothill Alligator Lizard (*G. multicarinatus*)

Mammals

* Mule Deer (*Odocoileus h. hemionus*)
* Black-tailed Deer (*O. h. columbianus*)
* Coyote (*Canis latrans*)
* Grey Fox (*Urocyon cinereoargenteus*)
    Common Opossum (*Didelphis marsupialis*)
    Raccoon (*Procyon lotor*)
    Adorned Shrew (*Sorex ornatus*)
    Striped Skunk (*Mephitis mephitis*)
* Black-tailed Jack Rabbit (*Lepus californicus*)
* Audubon Cottontail (*Sylvilagus audubonii*)
* Broad-handed Mole (*Scapanus latimanus*)
* Botta Pocket Gopher (*Thomomys bottae*)
* California Meadow Mouse (*Microtus californicus*)
* Western Harvest Mouse (*Reithrodontomys megalotis*)
* White-footed Deer Mouse (*Peromyscus maniculatus*)
    California Ground Squirrel (*Otospermophilus beecheyi*)
    House Mouse (*Mus musculus*)

Field Exercise #7

Name _____
Score _____

List the common plants characteristic of the Grasslands. Note the season and which plants are "flowering."

Season _____

1.   11.
2.   12.
3.   13.
4.   14.
5.   15.
6.   16.
7.   17.
8.   18.
9.   19.
10.   20.

List the animals seen on this trip.

Invertebrates   "Herps"   Birds and Mammals

Invertebrates:
1. 2. 3. 4. 5. 6. 7. 8. 9. 10. 11. 12. 13. 14. 15.

"Herps":
1. 2. 3. 4. 5.

Birds and Mammals:
1. 2. 3. 4. 5. 6. 7. 8. 9. 10. 11. 12. 13. 14. 15. 16. 17. 18. 19. 20.

Field Exercise #8   Name_____

                                           Score_____

Write a short essay on the morphological, physiological or behavioral adaptations necessary to "allow" an organism to invade and maintain itself in the Grasslands Biome.

THE BROADLEAF FORESTS

The four different types of broadleaf forests may be, in themselves, quite different geologically, meteorologically, and biologically. Their one common characteristic is that the majority of the trees found growing in these areas have broad, flat leaves. Generally speaking, the broadleaf forest exhibits four distinct seasons.

During the spring months, young, bright green leaves appear. New stems sprout, and flower buds begin to form. Summer in the broadleaf forest is generally characterized by the blossoming of the flowers and fruit formation. The leaves reach their maximum in size and growth. Long, hot days, interrupted by brief showers are excellent for maximum food production by photosynthesis. Undergrowth is dense, and the forest is lush. By fall, the leaves begin to wilt, dry up and fall off the trees. In some areas, this is, perhaps, the most beautiful of seasons. As the trees begin to shut off the water and mineral supply to the leaves, the leaves begin to turn beautiful shades of red, yellow, and brown. The undergrowth begins to die back as the forest prepares for winter. The winter months in a broadleaf forest are practically barren of color. The tree branches have dropped their leaves, and stand bare and dead-like against the sky. The undergrowth has died back to a tangle of twigs and branches and there is a uniform, gray drabness about the forest.

With the wide variety of broadleaf forests, each with its four seasons of presentation, it would seem quite misleading to attempt one composite description labeled "broadleaf forests." However, to discuss each type of forest in each of its four seasonal phases separately would constitute a stupendous undertaking. Therefore we will limit our discussion to only the four types of broadleaf forests that are found in the San Francisco Bay Area, and in their most distinctive "phase." It should be remembered, however, that these four may overlap extensively, and may also be intermixed with other types of biotic environments. Where appropriate, we will discuss seasonal changes pertinent to each species of organism.

The four types of broadleaf forests to be discussed here can actually be classified into two main groups: the Riparian (or Streamside) Woodland, and the Oak Woodlands. The Oak Woodlands can, however, be further divided into three distinct categories: The Northern Oak, Southern Oak, and Foothill Oak Woodlands. Each of these three Oak forests has distinct physical and biological characteristics. For brevity's sake, we will discuss these three under the more general heading of Oak Woodlands with species distinction where necessary.

   The Riparian Woodlands are usually found in stream valleys at the base
of hills and are shaded, except at midday, by those hills. Temperatures
are usually much cooler than the surrounding hills, winds are light breezes
or almost non-existent. Shade is abundant and, due to the proximity of
the stream, or water source, moisture is relatively high. The ground
is damp, cool, and usually quite rich in organic materials. Animal life
is abundant both in variety of types and numbers of individuals.

Riparian Woodlands

There are numerous examples of riparian woodlands in San Mateo County and on the San Francisco Peninsula. We will mention two accessible locations. The first is found by driving east from Skyline Blvd. along Crystal Springs Road to the Alameda de las Pulgas in San Mateo. This road starts at the Crystal Springs Dam and follows the San Mateo Creek eastward into Hillsborough.

The second riparian woodland to be discussed is the portion of Sawyer Camp Road in the San Francisco Water Company's watershed area that runs south from San Andreas Lake to Lower Crystal Spring Reservoir. However, the northern-most portion of this road passes through a foothill woodland type of area, while the road further to the south along the eastern edge of lower Crystal Springs Reservoir passes through Southern Oak Woodland and Savanna.

The riparian, or streamside, woodland is characterized most by the presence of willows. These plants are indicators of moist, deep soil, a high degree of shade, cooler temperatures, and less evaporation. Riparian woodlands occur along the banks of either intermittent or permanent streams. Since these usually occur in valleys, the riparian woodlands can usually be seen following the valley between two hills, or around the edges of fresh water lakes.

There are 6 species of willow common to our area. The most common willow growing in our local riparian woodlands is the Arroyo Willow (*Salix lasiolepis*). The Arroyo Willows are shrub-like trees which usually do not

Female   Male
Catkin   Catkin

Willow

Seed

Big Leaf Maple

Oregon Ash

exceed 15 feet in height. The simple leaves are about 5 inches long, irregularly lanceolate, and have entire rolled-under margins. The yellow flowers which bloom each spring grow on erect stems in bunches called Catkins. Willow trees usually grow in dense stands. This allows for the utilization of these trees by birds and other animals as nesting and feeding places relatively free from predation.

Growing alongside the willows is a taller tree which grows to 60 feet. It is the Big Leaf Maple (*Acer macrophyllum*). This tree has some of the biggest leaves of any common local plant. The leaves may exceed 10" in length and 6"-8" in breadth. The simple leaf is deeply lobed and serrated. They attach opposite one another on the stem. This opposite attachment to the stem differentiates the Maple from both the Sycamore and the Liquidamber, which have alternate leaf arrangement. The flowers grow in drooping clusters and mature, after fertilization, into wing-shaped fruit. These large trees provide food and nesting places for many birds and other animals. Maple trees lose their leaves in the late fall, and therefore, are deciduous as are most of the trees in the riparian woodland.

Several species of Ash (*Fraxinus spp.*) are found in our streamside woodlands. All are characterized by having pinnately compound leaves about 8-10 inches long. There are from 4 to 7 leaflets on each leaf. The Oregon Ash (*Fraxinus latifolia*) is more common in our watershed.

Another compound-leafed plant is the California Buckeye (*Aesculus californica*). This tree has palmately compound leaves rather than being pinnately compound like the ashes. The buckeye is not restricted to the riparian woodlands, and may also be found in the northern oak and foothill woodlands as well. The flowers grow in clusters like white plumes on erect stems. After fertilization, these flowers develop into large, pear-shaped fruits called "Horse Chestnuts." This fruit can be eaten by rodents, birds, and hungry nature lovers.

Buckeye

The California Laurel or Bay (*Umbellularia californica*) is the "Myrtle" of the Bible. The large (3-5 inch) dark green, smooth leaves can be dried and used as a seasoning in cooking. The trees grow to about 30 feet and have smooth bark. One of the largest California laurels in the state grows just off Sawyer Camp Road in the San Francisco watershed, in San Mateo County.

The tall, slender Poplars or Cottonwoods, of the genus Populus also follow the stream-bed through the Riparian Woodlands. These trees have spade-shaped simple leaves with flattened petioles. The flowers grow in soft cottony masses, or catkins. After fruit formation, this light, cottony material aids in the wind dispersal of seeds. A whole stand of Lombardy Poplars (*Populus nigra italica*) grows at the base of the Crystal Springs Dam and along San Mateo Creek in San Mateo County. These tall, slender, deciduous trees are planted throughout the Bay Area as wind breaks.

California Bay Laurel

The shrubs growing beneath the trees are also indicative of the moist nature of the riparian environment. The Creek Dogwood (*Cornus californica*) is a hardwood shrub. The bark appears smooth and is purplish-red in color. During the winter when these plants lose their leaves, the purple stems distinguish the Creek Dogwood from the Poison Oak. The small (1/8 inch) flowers grow in clusters like small bouquets. The dark green leaves have unique, curving lateral veins running from the midvein toward the edge and tip of the blade.

The Blue Elderberry (*Sambucus mexicana*) is a shrub-like tree that grows from four to ten feet in height. It has a pinnately compound leaf with from five to nine leaflets. The leaflets are serrated and pointed. The small bluish-white flowers grow in a flattened bunch upon several stems called a cyme. These flowers form delicious blue berries about 1/4" in diameter. Jams, jellies, and even wines are made from this small fruit.

Lombardy Poplars

Creek Dogwood

Elderberry

The Common Snowberry (*Symphori-carpos albus*) grows in shrubby masses along moist slopes. The light yellow-ish-green leaves are almost round, and stand out from the erect stems on thin petioles. This shrub produces many small (1/2" diameter) white berries from tiny, pink, bell-shaped flowers. The Snowberry is tasteless and somewhat pithy.

Snowberry

A low-growing vine common to this moist streamside community is the Wild Grape (*Vitis californica*). This soft, thin, pretty vine can exceed 50 feet in length, and its tendrils allow it to grow over and among other shrubs and trees. The vines produce maple-like leaves which are palmately veined into three main lobes. The vines pro-duce greenish-white flowers during the early summer. The purple berries become edible during the early fall months.

Other vines growing in the riparian woodland which should not be confused with the Wild Grape are the Wild Cu-cumber (*Marah fabaceus*) and the West-ern Wild Cucumber (*M. oreganus*). These vines also have large maple-like leaves, but the palmate veination forms five to seven lobes rather than the three for the grape. Wild Cucum-bers have flowers similar to the Wild Grape, but instead of forming soft, purple grapes, the fruit of the Wild Cucumber is a spiny, dry, bitter-tasting fruit about an inch and a half in diameter.

Wild Cucumber

Coyote Bush, Poison Oak, Toyon, and many wild flowers of the chaparral and grasslands also grow in the ripar-ian woodland. The Sword Fern (*Poly-stichum munitum*) and the Western

Sword Fern

Bracken Fern (*Pteridium aquilinum*) of the cone forests usually grow in abundance in this moist area. However, all of these plants have been discussed elsewhere in detail.

One noticeable plant that should be pointed out at this time is the Hoary Nettle (*Urtica holosericae*). This nettle is a low (1-3 foot), herbaceous, single-stemmed plant with broad, simple, deeply serrated leaves about 3 inches in length. These leaves are covered with a fuzzy material (pubescence) that causes a very painful burning sensation if brushed against one's skin. This burning may last for several hours or longer. The "burning" sensation is actually a physiological reaction of the skin to the injection of a plant protein into the skin. As with all protein reactions, different people will respond with varying degrees of discomfort. If the pain or swelling becomes excessive, or lasts for an extended duration, a physician should be consulted. The best advice is to stay away from the Nettles.

Bracken Fern

Hoary Nettle

Goldenback Fern

The common Spearmint (*Mentha spicata*) can be differentiated from the Hoary Nettle by the characteristic square stems of the mint family. The leaves are quite similar in appearance to the nettle, but are not nearly so fuzzy (pubescent) as that stinging plant. Spearmint is edible—nettles definitely are NOT!

Wild, or Flowering Currant (*Ribes glutinosum*) has a typical grape-type leaf, but the plant grows erect (5'-6') instead of prostrate in vine fashion. The leaves are about 2 inches across, and are soft. The Red or White flowers give way in the summer to edible fruit.

The Spreading, or Common Rushes (*Juncus patens*) produce rounded, dark green, stem-like leaves which rise out of the shallow water or damp soil from one to three feet. The brownish tufted 1/2 inch flowers are produced in the summer and fall and grow on the upper part of the plant. The simple un-branched "stems" grow from rhizomes, or underground stems.

Mint

Wild Currant

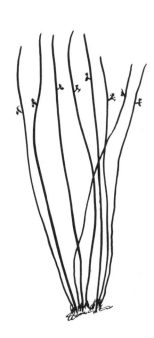

Spreading Rushes

Cattails

Cattails (*Typha latifolia*) usually grow out from the shore in shallow water. Their 1 1/2" wide, flat-bladed leaves grow out of the base of the stem. The leaves and naked flower-bearing stem sometimes reach heights in excess of six feet. The flowers grow in brownish tufts or erect spikes at the tip of the stem. Male flowers and female flowers are produced on the same stem, with the male flowers forming the tip of the spike. Muskrats and beavers utilize the roots and leaves for food and home-building materials. Red-winged Blackbirds eat the seeds and build their nests in dense stands of Cattails.

Filimentous green algae, flowering Duckweed (*Lemna spp.*), pond scums, and many microscopic plants provide food, oxygen and shelter for the smaller aquatic animals common in the streams of our area.

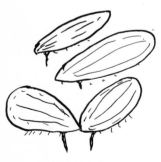

Duckweed

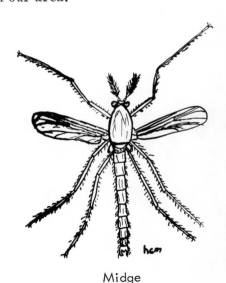

Midge

Many animals live on, in, or under the raparian plants. Most of the animals, with the exception of birds, are nocturnal or secretive, and are, therefore, very difficult to observe. With patience and ingenuity, most of the major mammals, reptiles, and larger invertebrate animals which abound in this moist area and in the water can be seen. We strongly recommend that anyone interested in these smaller types of animals carry a fine mesh dip net, butterfly net, and a good reference book of invertebrates to the field with them.

We will just briefly mention the most obvious insects, both adult and larval forms, found in, on, or over the surface of streams. This is by no means even an attempt to list all of the insects, or to give a complete description of the over 800,000 species. To aid in identification, note the bibliography plus the pictures of the insects mentioned below.

You will probably see many insects flying over the surface of the water. Most of these are small mosquitos, gnats, and midges. These numerous small insects provide food for many birds as well as for the large and beautiful dragon-flies and damsel-flies. These big, bright adult Odonota rest on weeds with their two pair of wings held out horizontally (dragon-flies) or back along the body (damsel-flies). They fly through swarms of small insects catching them in basket-like legs. The larvae of the damsel-flies and dragon-flies scurry about on the bottom of the stream, and among the weeds, feeding on small fish and other larval and adult aquatic forms.

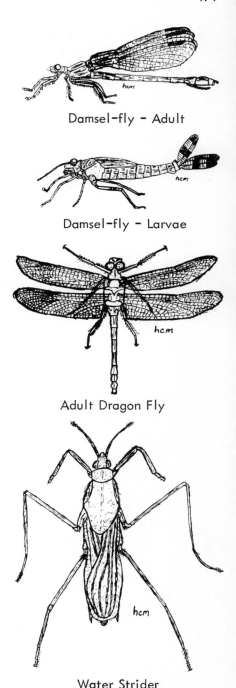

Damsel-fly – Adult

Damsel-fly – Larvae

Adult Dragon Fly

Water Strider

A FIELD GUIDE TO THE NATURAL HISTORY
OF THE SAN FRANCISCO BAY AREA

On or near the surface of the waters are Water Striders (Gerridae), Water Boatman (Corixidae), Back Swimmers (Notonectidae), Predaceous Diving Beetles (Dytiscidae) and Whirligig Beetles (Gyrinidae). Deeper in the water or on the bottom you can note the larvae of the above mentioned forms, plus the adult Giant Water Bugs (Belostomatidae).

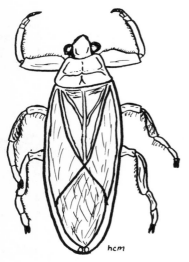

Giant Water Bug

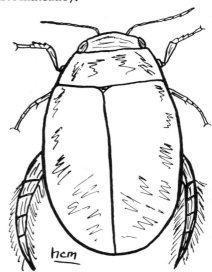

Predaceous Diving Beetle

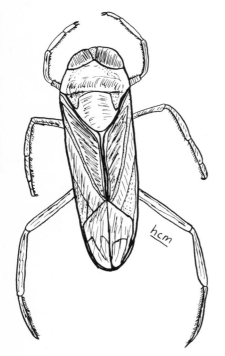

Back Swimmer

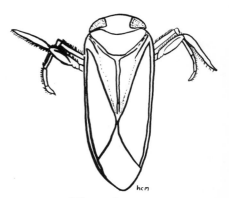

Water Boatman

Several types of small minnow-like fish can be found in these waters. Among these are the Stickle Backs (*Gasterosteus spp.*), and Mosquitofish (*Gambusia affinis*). These fish eat the larvae and adult insects, molluscs, worms, other small fish and some algae. They are in turn preyed upon by other larger fish.

Three-spined Stickle Back

Many amphibians and reptiles live in the moist confines of the stream-side woodland. The Red-legged Frog (*Rana aurora*) is probably the most common frog on the Peninsula. It is also the largest. The body measures up to five inches and the hind legs exceed the body in length. These hind legs are mottled brown on top and reddish-white underneath. The dorsal surfaces of the head and body are mottled brown while all ventral surfaces with the noted exception of the legs are white. This frog is usually found in or alongside of quiet waters.

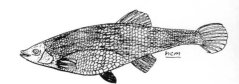

Mosquitofish

A somewhat smaller frog which frequents faster flowing streams is the Yellow-legged Frog (*Rana boylei*). Yellow-legged Frogs lack the two conspicuous dorso-lateral folds of skin running along the upper sides as seen in the Red-legged Frog. The inner portions of the hind legs are also a yellowish-white in place of the reddish-white of the larger frog. Adult Red- and Yellow-legged Frogs feed upon insects, smaller frogs, lizards, fish, etc., while the young, or tadpoles, feed upon algae and other water plants. The frogs, in turn, are preyed upon by the herons, large fish, raccoons, and other carnivores.

Red-legged Frog

Yellow-legged Frog

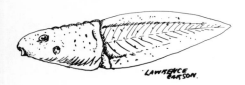

Tadpole

Green Tree Frog

Western Toad

The little Green Tree Frog, or Pacific Tree Frog (*Hyla regilla*), is the most arboreal frog on the peninsula. Adult tree frogs can be seen and/or heard calling from the trees growing near the streams. While Green Tree Frogs are most commonly green, many adults are brown. Contrary to popular belief, based upon research done with other species of tree frogs, the Pacific Tree Frog can not change from brown to green. There are brown ones and there are green ones. They can, however, lighten or darken themselves considerably in response to environmental or physiological changes. Both brown and green individuals have a black stripe running along both sides of the head and through the eyes. The *Hyla* are the smallest frogs on the San Francisco Peninsula, and are the only ones with expanded toe pads which allow them to cling to vertical surfaces. These small amphibians are insect eaters. They, in turn, serve as food for fish, snakes, birds, raccoons, and other predators.

The Western Toad (*Bufo boreas*) is a squat, warty frog-like amphibian. Toads are distinguished from frogs primarily by the length of the hind legs, and body morphology. The hind legs of the toads are just slightly longer than the front legs. This allows toads to walk, whereas frogs are restricted to hopping. The Western Toad has a much thicker skin than frogs. This characteristic allows toads to roam far from the water source in which they must lay their eggs. Adult toads are carnivorous, eating other toads, frogs, insects, slugs, small snakes, etc., and, in turn, are eaten by red-legged frogs, kingsnakes, garter-snakes, hawks, herons, and other predators.

One of our most common sala-manders is the California Newt (*Taricha torosa*). This animal grows to about 5"-6", has a thick, rough, red-dish-brown skin on its back and is yellowish to orange underneath. This animal hides in the water, under rocks, leaves, and other debris. The tadpole-like larvae hatch from small jelly-like clusters of eggs. The larvae eat algae and other small plant materials. Adult newts eat insects, worms and snails.

California Newt

The Arboreal Salamanders (*Aneides lugubris*) can also be found in our ra-parian woodland near trees or small streams. They hide under leaves, logs, in wood rat nests, or along the edges of waterways. This salamander is about 7" long, is plain brown with small yellow dots scattered over its back. This animal eats ants, beetles, centipedes, or any insect larvae avail-able to it. The Arboreal Salamander lays its eggs in trees on small stalks.

Arboreal Salamander

A small worm-like salamander common to streamside areas, chapar-ral, and oak forests is the California Slender Salamander (*Batrachoseps attenuatus*). This small 2-5 inch, brown amphibian lives under leaf lit-ter, bark and in the soil where, if discovered, it will snap and wiggle like a worm. This salamander has tiny legs which can be used for walk-ing but if in a hurry it will move like a snake. The Slender Salamander eats small insects, worms, pill bugs, and other small larvae.

California Slender Salamander

Aquatic

Land-dwelling

Western Garter Snake

Rubber Boa

Western Skink

The most common snake in the raparian woodland is the Common Garter Snake (*Thamnophis sirtalis*). It grows to 2 1/2 - 3 feet and is a dirty black with a yellowish stripe on its back running from head to tail. Reddish blotches are commonly found on the sides and the belly is lighter. This snake is brighter, and much more aquatic than the terrestrial or Western Garter Snake (*T. elegans*), which is also found here, but it lacks the bright yellow stripe. Garter Snakes eat lizards, toads, frogs, and small mammals. These snakes in turn, provide food for bullfrogs, hawks, and mammalian carnivores.

Other common snakes are the Western Ring-Necked Snake and the Racers, both mentioned in the chapter on the grasslands, and the Rubber Boa (*Charina bottae*). The Boa grows to only 2 feet and has a characteristic body that is thick and blunt, at both ends. Boas hide in leaf litter where their reddish brown body is easily concealed. Like all boas the Rubber Boa kills primarily by constriction. It eats lizards, and small mammals, but will take insects, worms, and spiders. This snake is very docile and can be easily handled.

Only a few lizards are commonly found in streamside woodlands. They are the Western Fence Lizard, the Northern Alligator Lizard, both previously mentioned, and the Western Skink (*Eumeces skiltonianus*). The skink has a shiny light brown body with yellowish lines on its back and a blue tail, usually in the young, but also in some adult animals. The skink grows 5 to 7 inches long and must be

handled carefully. If roughly handled
the tail will fall off and wiggle wildly.
This is a protective device used to
distract predators. The skink can be
found nesting in the day under rocks,
boards, and in the leaf litter. They
hunt at night feeding on insects, pill
bugs, and spiders.

Two diurnal mammals usually seen
in the trees, or on the ground under
the trees, are the Fox Squirrels and
the Grey Squirrels. The Western Grey
Squirrel (*Sciurus griseus*) is larger
and more common. It is uniformly
grey along the head, back, and legs,
with all ventral, or belly surfaces a
soft white. The long, fluffy, grey tail
is usually held in a high arch over the
back. These animals do not have cheek
pouches for temporary storage of food
as do many of its close relatives. Grey
Squirrels spend most of their life high
up in the branches of oaks and pine
trees, where they build their nests in
abandoned flicker or woodpecker holes.
Grey Squirrels eat primarily acorns
in the trees but do occasionally roam
the ground in search of nuts or fruit.

The Fox Squirrel (*Sciurus niger*)
is a rusty red-grey across the back,
shoulders and head, while the belly is
a yellowish-red. The Fox Squirrel is
not nearly as nimble a climber as the
Grey Squirrel and often appears rather
clumsy as it jumps from limb to limb.
This squirrel tends to endure close
contact with man somewhat better than
its grey cousin, and can often be seen
in back yards. Fox Squirrels are primarily tree dwellers, eating the seeds
and fruit, and nesting in large clumps
of assembled twigs and leaves high off
the ground.

Grey Squirrel

Fox Squirrel

Two nocturnal mammals common to the raparian woodlands are the Common Opossum (*Didelphis marsupialis*) and the Raccoon (*Procyon lotor*). The Raccoon is the largest mammal (2-3 feet) commonly found in the raparian woodland. It is also the easiest to identify with its black-and-white ringed tail and black mask over the eyes. The Raccoon is an omnivore eating frogs, lizards, crayfish, fruits, seeds, and birds' eggs. They are also scavengers and often raid campsites and garbage cans. The females nest in hollow trees where both sexes sleep during the day. Raccoons have human-like forepaws and leave characteristic footprints in the soft earth or mud around the stream. This animal, like most nocturnal animals such as the cougars and foxes, has a reflecting layer behind the retinas of the eyes. This layer, the tapetum lucidum, reflects the beam of flashlights and car headlights causing the eyes to appear to shine.

Raccoon

The Opossum is the only North American marsupial, or pouched animal. It is slightly smaller than the Raccoon (2 to 2 1/2 feet), but is more heavily built. The Opossum has a grayish-white head and a bare, prehensil, scaly tail. The body of the animal is covered with long straight gray hair. Its pointed snout covers a full set of teeth allowing it an omnivorus diet. The hind feet have short, clawless halixs, or "big toes" that extend inward toward each other. A new-born litter of 20-25 Opossums would hardly cover a silver dollar. These young are not completely formed

Opossum

at birth, but must find their way up the
belly of the mother and into the pouch,
or marsupium, where development
continues for about two more months.

The raparian woodland also harbors
some of the smallest mammals of San
Mateo County: the Shrews (*Sorex spp.*).
The Shrews seldom exceed four inches
in length. They are primarily nocturnal insect-eaters, and have a well
developed set of teeth. The most distinguishing characteristics of Shrews
are the small size, sharply pointed,
bristled snout, small eyes, and short
legs. These animals have one of the
highest metabolic rates of any mammal and therefore, require relatively
huge quantities of food. Some have
been known to eat their weight in insects every few hours! The most common Shrews found in the streamside
woodland are the Vagrant Shrews (*Sorex
vagrans*), Ornate Shrews (*S. ornatus*),
and the Trowbridge Shrews (*S. trowbridgii*).

Another nocturnal, insect-eating,
small mammal is the bat. Several
different types of bats can be seen flying erratically back and forth above
the surface of the water, and through
the branches of the trees, just before
and just after dark. Bats are not flying rats and mice, as some people be-
lieve, nor do they fly into women's
hair or suck blood. Most bats are
strictly insect eaters. In view of their
diet, it would seem obvious that bats
are important insect pest control
agents, and should not be destroyed.
The most common bats of the raparian
woodlands are the Little Brown Bats
(*Myotis lucifugus*) with a wingspread

Trowbridge Shrew

Red Bat

Hairy-winged Bat

of from eight to ten inches, and the
Pallid Bats (*Antrozous pallidus*) with
a 12"-14" wingspread, and the Red
Bat (*Lasiurus borealis*) with a 16"
wingspan. This last bat nests in trees,
while most other bats roost in caves
or buildings.

The Dusky-footed Wood Rat (*Neotoma
fuscipes*), a common rodent in this
area, is a light brown over the back
and dorsal surfaces, and white underneath, and is one of the largest rodents
in the area (16" in total length). Unlike the city-dwelling black rat, the
woodrat is a relatively clean rodent.
It builds its large dome-shaped nest
out of sticks and insulates its woodland home with whatever the rodent
finds available. This nest-building
habit has resulted in the nickname of
"pack-rat." Many a camper's glove
or other bright objects have become
insulation for the woodrat's home.
The woodrat is a carrier of the disease
known as Sylvatic Plague and other
diseases. However, its tendency to
avoid contact with humans reduces its
danger to man as a vector of illness.
These animals eat nearly anything
available, but are primarily seed,
nut, and fruit eaters. The woodrats,
in turn, serve as food for the Great
Horned Owl, Bobcats, Coyotes, and
other nocturnal carnivores.

The White-footed Deer Mouse (*Peromyscus maniculatus*) is about the size
of a house mouse (3 to 4 inches), but
is completely white along all under-
surfaces and legs. Its large ears,
and longer tail (over 2/3 length of
body) distinguishes it from most other
mice. The White-footed Deer Mouse

Wood Rat

Deer Mice

is the most widely distributed mouse in California. Like all rodents, it is primarily a seed-eater but will take other foods.

One of the smaller (13-18 inches) cat-sized carnivores found in the raparian woodlands is the attractive Striped Skunk (*Mephitis mephitis*). This nocturnal mammal is black with large, white stripes running the length of its body and fluffy tail. The white stripes merge into a white cap on the head. Like all skunks, the Striped Skunk can discharge a foul-smelling spray up to fifteen feet. This oily liquid is emitted from two rectal glands at the base of the tail and can temporarily blind an opponent. Skunks eat mice, crayfish, baby birds, insects, and occasionally fruits and seeds. The Striped Skunk lives in burrows, under logs, or in caves. They give birth to one litter of about six young each spring. Automobiles are perhaps the number one predator of skunks.

The most obvious form of animal life in the raparian woodland is the bird life. Birds utilize these woods for feeding, nesting, and hiding areas. Most of the birds to be seen here are relatively small and diurnal. They may be approached rather closely if one is patient and quiet. The birds feeding in or around the edges of the water are the small herons, bitterns and wood ducks.

Two herons commonly seen wading through the shallows of streams searching for a fish, frogs, and tadpoles, are the Green Heron (*Butorides virescens*) and the Black-crowned Night Heron (*Nycticorax nycticorax*). The

Striped Skunk

Muskrat

Green Heron

Night Heron

American Bittern

Wood Duck

Green Heron is about the size of a slim chicken when the bird is standing (sometimes on one foot). The head is pulled down between the shoulders. This head has a black "Cap" and reddish "Cheeks." The body of the bird is grayish green. The green legs are about the length of the body and rather slim. This is our smallest heron being only the size of a crow.

The Black-crowned Night Heron is slightly larger than the Green Heron, has longer legs, and a distinctive black cap and cape over the neck and shoulders. The cheeks and chest are white and the body is gray. Several long white feathers grow backwards from the head reaching the shoulders. Both of these herons fly with the slow wing beat characteristic of all herons. When flying, the head is held back between the shoulders and the feet are extended backwards. Both of these herons nest among the willows that grow near or in the water. The Night Heron forages primarily at night as its name implies.

Another heron-like bird is the American Bittern (*Botaurus lentiginosus*). This stocky, brown wading bird is distinguished by obvious vertical bars of alternating dark and light brown on the breast. The rest of the body is a light yellowish-brown. Bitterns eat insects, insect larvae, tadpoles, water spiders, small fish, frogs, and salamanders. The nest of this bird is built among the marsh reeds and tall grasses.

Wood Ducks (*Aix sponsa*) are brightly colored birds and are unique waterfowl. They inhabit woodlands, building their nests in hollow trees. These birds sometimes dabble for submerged foods, but occasionally feed upon dry land for acorns and other seeds, plants, etc. This is probably the only duck we will encounter in the Raparian or Oak Woodland.

Many smaller birds may be seen feeding and foraging low over the surface of the water. Some of these birds nest in the streamside willows, reeds, or grasses while others nest further from the water. Most of these birds are insect eaters, catching their prey on the wing. The Violet-green Swallow (*Tachycineta thalassina*) nests in hollow trees some distance from the stream but forages low over the water for mosquitos, gnats, and other flying insects. These birds are distinguished by short, sharp-pointed, back-swept wings which enable rapid, erratic flight, and a pretty purple, green and white coloration. It has a green back, two white spots on the violet rump and a white face and belly. The two white rump patches distinguish this bird from the Tree Swallow (*Iridoprocne bicolor*). Otherwise, the Tree Swallows and the Violet-green Swallows are very similar. Both of these birds usually forage early in the morning and late afternoon.

Another flying insect-eater is the resident Black Phoebe (*Sayornis nigricans*). This is the only black flycatcher in our area. The white belly is the only contrasting (non-black) marking. This bird is usually seen perched on the tip of cattails or reeds close to the water. They occasionally fly up and out, take an insect, and return to the same or to nearby reeds. These feeding flights are usually short,

Violet-green Swallow

Tree Swallow

Black Phoebe

Western Flycatcher

Cedar Waxwing

not exceeding 10 to 15 feet. This is a typical fly-catcher feeding pattern.

The Western Flycatcher (*Empidonax difficilis*) is a small flycatcher being somewhat smaller than a sparrow. It is olive-brown in color, with a yellowish belly, and a white ring around the eye. Several other flycatchers may be observed, but this one is the most widely distributed throughout the county and, indeed, the whole western United States.

Many birds feed and forage among the branches of the willows and shrubs, while others feed primarily on the ground and among the leaf litter. The majority of birds foraging among the branches feed upon crawling or burrowing insects, insect larvae, and spiders. They may be seen hopping or flitting from branch to branch, occasionally pecking at the bark. The ground foraging birds are primarily seed eating. An exception to this is the Thrush which feeds by probing among the leaf litter for insects.

The Hermit Thrush (*Hylocichla guttata*) is smaller than his cousin,

Hermit Thrush

the Robin, and has black speckles on its breast. It is rusty brown above and has a whitish belly. The Varied Thrush (*Ixoreus naevius*) is about the size of a Robin, but has orange markings above the eyes and orange wing bars. It also has a black band across the breast. The Robin (*Turdus migratorius*), needs no introduction to most readers. It has a charcoal black back, rusty red breast, and a yellow bill. Thrushes are actually omnivores, eating worms, insect larvae, berries, and seeds.

Varied Thrush

The Brewer Blackbird (*Euphagus cyanocephalus*) is a ground feeding, seed and insect eater. It is about the size of a Robin, but this male blackbird is jet black, almost irridescent, with a bright yellow eye ring. The females are brownish and lack the eye ring. This bird is found in almost all biomes of the San Francisco Peninsula.

The California Valley Quail (*Lophortyx californicus*) is the state bird of California. It is a ground feeding, seed-eating bird that is slightly larger than a Robin. Quails have stout bodies and relatively short legs. The Valley Quail has a forward-curved, feathery topnot growing out of the forehead.

Robin

Brewer's Blackbird

California Quail

LAWRENCE
CARSON

Song Sparrow

Green-backed Goldfinch

The males have a larger topnot and an obviously black throat, and white forehead. These birds usually forage in flocks, or coveys, of 15 to 25 birds. Quail roost in the trees, but can often be seen "dusting" themselves in drier, open areas during the day.

The Song Sparrow (*Melospiza melodia*) is our only sparrow with a black spot on its striped breast. It is generally brown with gray streaks. Like all sparrows, the Song Sparrow is a ground feeding seed eater. These birds usually do not aggregate in flocks, but may be seen in pairs.

Two of the prettiest small sparrow-sized birds of the Raparian Woodland are the Green-backed Goldfinch and the Common or American Goldfinch. The Green-backed Goldfinch (*Spinus psaltria*) has a yellow belly and greenish-yellow back. It also has a black forehead and wing. The American, or Common Goldfinch, (*Spinus tristis*) is similar except the yellow color extends over the crown, head, neck, and back. Both of these birds are seed-eaters with typical sparrow-like bills.

Those birds which normally forage and feed primarily in the branches usually have slimmer bills than the seed-eating ground feeders. Most of these ground feeders are insect-eaters, but some do eat berries and other fruit.

The Warblers are the songsters of the Raparian Woodlands. While the Goldfinches have a beautiful song, the Warblers' calls are more varied and soft. The most common Warbler along our streams is the Pileolated Warbler (*Wilsonia pusilla*). The males are slightly greenish-yellow with a bright

yellow breast and head. It is distinguished from the Green-backed Goldfinch by its slender insect-eating bill,
black cap (not forehead), and wings
that are uniform in color. With its
slender beak Warblers usually eat insects found on the leaves and bark,
but they can take flying insects.

The Bewick's Wren (*Thryomanes
bewickii*) is a small (much smaller
than a sparrow) insect-eating bird.
Their long, slender, slightly down-
curved bill is used to probe into the
bark and leaves for food. Like all
wrens, it holds its tail in a smartly
perked-up position when the bird is
perching. It is distinguished from
other wrens by a distinctive white line
over each eye.

The House Wren (*Troglodytes aedon*)
is also found in these woodlands. They
are slightly larger, about 4 inches,
are gray-brown above but lack the white
markings seen in the Bewick's Wren.

The Hutton's Vireo (*Vireo huttoni*)
is about the size of a Warbler, but with
a short, slender bill. It is a greenish-
gray in color, and has a white ring
partially around each eye, and two
white wing bars. Vireos move through
the bushes from branch to branch in
a slow, deliberate motion as they look
for their food.

Many, many other birds are found
in the Raparian Woodlands along with
many more mammals and reptiles,
insects, and spiders. However, most
of the remaining animals and plants
can also be found in the Hardwood
"Oak" Forests to be discussed next.

American Goldfinch

Pileolated Warbler

Bewick's Wren

House Wren

Flicker

Yellow-throated Vireo

Bushtit

Western Tanager

Scrub Jay

Brown Towhee

Belted Kingfisher

The three <u>Oak Woodlands</u> differ from the Raparian Woodlands in several ways. These differences are caused primarily by the much lower water content of the soil in Oak Woodlands. As mentioned in the introduction to this chapter, Oak Woodlands differ among themselves also. Major causal factors in these differences are soil moisture and depth, exposure to sun and wind, proximity to the coast, temperature, and altitude.

<u>Foothill Woodlands</u> are closest to the Raparian Woodlands in moisture and depth of soil. This allows for the growth of tall trees with spreading branches. The deep shade resulting from the trees, however, retards underbrush growth.

The <u>Northern Oak Woodlands</u> are slightly drier than the Foothill Woodlands, and the trees are separated allowing sunlight to reach the ground. A dense tangle of chaparral-like brush results in these partially open areas.

The <u>Southern Oak Woodlands</u> are the driest of the Hardwood Forests and very closely resemble Savannas in geology and meteorology.

Foothill Woodlands. Northern segment of Sawyer Camp Road.

The Foothill Oak Woodlands may be seen along both sides of Sawyer Camp Road from the southern end of San Andreas Lake southward about one mile until the road passes into a Raparian Woodland area. This area is characterized by high, spreading broadleaf trees and low, shade-tolerant undergrowth. The trees usually form a complete canopy over the ground. This creates a shadowed, almost rain forest effect. Characteristic trees are the Buckeye, California Bay or Laurel, and Live Oak.

Mixed Northern Oak Woodlands west of Crystal
Springs Lake, San Mateo, California.

The Northern Oak Woodland is usually characterized by dense, high, undergrowth. It is inhabited by a wide variety of vegetation, mammals, and birds. These woodlands can usually be found running through lower hills and occasionally semi-open valleys. Skyline Blvd. south of Palo Alto all the way to Santa Cruz, exhibits one of the most interesting stands of Northern Oak Woodlands on the San Francisco Peninsula. Characteristic plants are the Black Oaks, Blue Oaks, Oregon Oak, and Interior Live Oak.

There are numerous examples of Southern Oak Woodlands in San Mateo County, but for convenience sake we will use an area already mentioned; namely, the southern portion of Sawyer Camp Road. As this private road (open to the public during daylight hours only) passes southward along lower Crystal Springs Reservoir, the surrounding vegetation changes from the moist Raparian Woodlands to open Savanna country and terminates on Skyline Boulevard just opposite the western-most terminus of Crystal Springs Road. The lower hills east of La Canada Road north of Woodside and the Searsville Lake area also display the Southern Oak Woodland. Characteristically, these areas are primarily grasslands and savanna, with widely separated Black Oaks and Coast Live Oaks.

Southern Oak Woodlands

With few exceptions most of the common plants and animals that are found in the three Hardwood forest areas are the same, or similar to, organisms found in nearby or adjoining biomes. Many of the plants and animals have already been mentioned in the previous two chapters, the first part of this chapter, or will be mentioned in the next chapter. Only those plants and animals that are restricted to the hardwood forests or those organisms not yet mentioned will now be discussed. A plant check list, by forest type, will be included at the end of this chapter.

The Blue Oak (*Quercus douglasii*)
is a tree that grows to about 50 feet
in height. It has a smooth whitish
bark. The leaves are slightly lobed
and roundish, and grow to about 3
inches long. These leaves fall off
in the winter months. The acorns
serve as a food for squirrels, pigeons,
and even man. Indians and early settlers steamed the acorns to leach the
bitter tannin out of the seed, then they
ground them up to make mush.

The California Black Oak (*Quercus
kelloggii*) is one of the prettiest oaks
growing in California. Leaves of this
80 foot, deciduous tree appear in early
spring, and are reddish, fuzzy, and
soft. By midsummer the leaves turn
dark green and shiny above. The 5-6
inch leaf is deeply lobed, with each
lobe usually having three sharp points.
The California Black Oak serves as a
microhabitat for nearly all of the animals found in the oak forests. Large
mammals such as Raccoons and Opossums live in hollows in the tree. Grey
Squirrels build their nests among the
upper branches of the tree and feed
upon the acorns. Woodpeckers build
their nests in holes in the trunk of the
tree. Many other animals either nest
or forage in or on the branches and
leaves of this tree.

The Valley Oak (*Quercus lobata*
grows to more than 100 feet in height.
The long, narrow (6 inches by 3 inches)
dark yellow-green leaves have deep
rounded-lobed margins. The long
slender acorns grow to about 2-2 1/2
inches long and have bumpy caps covering the blunt, or stem end. The thick

Blue Oak

California Black Oak

bark is covered with light, checker-
board-like scales. These trees grow
most abundantly in drier areas such
as the Southern and Foothill Forests.

The Oregon Oak (*Quercus garryana*)
seldom exceeds 50 feet in height. Its
deeply-lobed leaves are nearly as broad
as they are long (6"x5"), and the lobes
are rounded rather than spiked. These
leaves are a uniform dark green on
top and a lighter gray-green beneath.
The acorns are nearly round, and are
topped with a full scaly cap. The whitish-gray, thin bark is checkered into
small plates. This oak grows primarily in the Northern Oak Forests such
as along Skyline Blvd. south of Huddart
Park, but is not very abundant any-
where in San Mateo. The lumber made
from Oregon Oaks is of great economic
value, and is used in the manufacture
of furniture, hard oak veneer, floor-
ing, and even long-lasting fence posts.

The two Evergreen Oaks most commonly found on the San Francisco Peninsula are the Coast Live Oak (*Quercus
agrifolia*) and the Interior Live Oak
(*Quercus wislizenii*). The Coast Live
Oak is probably the most common oak
on the Peninsula. Its 2" holly-like
leaves with its spiney edges curled
under cup-like resemble the darker
green holly leaf. This tree grows to
75 feet in height with heavy spreading
branches. The rounded, tear-drop
shaped acorn grows to about 1 1/2"
and has a scaly cap that covers the
broader half of the nut.

The Interior Live Oak (*Quercus
wislizenii*) grows to about 75 feet and
has thick, smooth bark. The 2 1/2"
leaves are similar to the Coast Live

Valley Oak

Oregon Oak

Coast Live Oak

Interior Live Oak

Oak, but the serrated edges do not cup under in a holly-like fashion. Some of the leaves may lack serration entirely, and have relatively smooth edges. The acorns of this tree are long (1 1/2") with a scaly cap covering the upper 1/3 of the nut. The Interior Live Oaks are not very common in San Mateo County, but may be found along several eastern slopes of the coastal ranges such as King Mountain west of the town of Woodside.

The trees just mentioned are indications of the various areas but are by no means the only trees to be found here. Some plants such as the Laurels, Madrones, Buckthorns, Wild Oats and Poison Oak are common in all three types of oak forests with the lower shrubs in greater evidence in the Northern Oak Forests. Thistles, Teasels, Soft Cheat, and Mouse Barley are more common to the Southern Oak Forest. Ferns and mosses grow freely in the shade of the Foothill Woodlands. Shrubs and low ground cover plants are most indicative of these various areas.

No single animal is totally restricted to only one type of the forests. Due to their mobility and adaptability, the same species of animal will be able to move from one forest to another forest or adjacent biome. Note the check lists for the most common plants and animals.

A Check List of Broadleaf Forest Plants and Animals.

Those with the asterisks are mentioned in this chapter.

Riparian or Streamside Woodland

Plants

* Western Bracken Fern (*Pteridium aquilina pubescens*)
* Sword Fern (*Polystichum munitum*)
* Goldenback Fern (*Pityrogramma triangularis*)
* Arroyo Willow (*Salix lasiolepis*)
* Big Leaf Maple (*Acer macrophyllum*)
  Western Sycamore (*Plantanus racemosa*)
* Oregon Ash (*Fraxinus latifolia*)
* California Buckeye (*Aesculus californica*)
* California Laurel or Bay (*Umbellularia californica*)
* Lombardy Poplars (*Populus nigra italica*)
  Fremont Cottonwood (*P. fremontii*)
  Black Cottonwood (*P. trichocarpa*)
* Creek Dogwood (*Cornus californica*)
* Blue Elderberry (*Sambucus mexicana*)
* Common Snowberry (*Symphoricarpos albus*)
* Wild Grape (*Vitis californica*)
* Wild Cucumber (*Marah fabaceus*)
* Western Wild Cucumber (*M. oreganus*)
* Hoary Nettle (*Urtica holosericea*)
* Common Spearmint (*Mentha spicata*)
* Flowering Currant (*Ribes glutinosum*)
* Common Rushes (*Juncus patens*)
* Common Cattail (*Typha latifolia*)
* Duckweeds (*Lemna spp.*)
  Pacific Bulrush (*Scirpus californicus*)
  Woolly Sedge (*Carex lanuginosa*)
  Wild Rose (*Rosa californica*)
  California Blackberry (*Rubus vitifolius*)
  Western Thimbleberry (*R. parviflorus*)
  Poison Oak (*Rhus diversiloba*)
  California Coffeeberry (*Rhamnus californica*)
  Blue-Blossom Ceanothus (*Ceanothus thrysiflorus*)

Plants (continued)

Madrone (*Arbutus menziesii*)
Monkey Flower (*Mimulus spp.*)
Sages (*Salvia spp.*)
Thistles (*Cirsium spp.*)
Spiney Clotbur (*Xanthium spinosum*)
White Alder (*Alnus rhombifolia*)
Coyote Bush (*Baccharis pilularis*)
Common Horsetail (*Equisetum arvense*)
Western Scouring Rush (*E. hyemale affine*)
Common Trillium (*Trillium chloropetalum*)
Slim Solomon (*Smilacina stellata*)
Miner's Lettuce (*Montia [Claytonia] perfoliata*)
Curley Dock (*Rumex crispus*)
Rabbit's Foot Grass (*Polypogon monspeliensis*)
Henderson Shooting Star (*Dodecantheon hendersoni*)

Foothill Woodland

Most Riparian plants are found here plus these indicator plants.

* Blue Oaks (*Quercus douglasii*)
* Valley Oak (*Q. lobata*)
* Coast Live Oak (*Q. agrifolia*)
* Interior Live Oak (*Q. wislizenii*)
  Madrone (*Arbutus menziesii*)
* California Buckeye (*Aesculus californica*)
* California Bay or Laurel (*Umbellularia californica*)
  Coffeeberry (*Rhamnus californica*)
* Sword Fern (*Polystichum munitum*)
* Western Bracken Fern (*Pteridium aquilina*)
  Poison Oak (*Rhus diversiloba*)
  Yerba Santa (*Eriodictyon californicum*)
  Western Leatherwood (*Dirca occidentalis*)
  Western Hound's Tongue (*Cynoglossum grande*)
  White Globe-Lily (*Calochortus albus*)

Northern Oak Woodlands

Most chaparral plants are found here plus these indicator plants.

* Black Oak   (*Quercus kelloggii*)
* Oregon Oak (*Q. garryana*)
* Blue Oak   (*Q. douglasi*)
* Interior Live Oak (*Q. wislizenii*)
  Golden Cup Oak   (*Q. chrysolepis*)
  Madrone (*Arbutus menziesii*)
  Manzanita (*Arctostaphylos spp.*)
  California Fremontia (*Fremontia californica*)
  Coyote Bush (*Baccharis pilularis*)
  California Sagebrush (*Artemisia californica*)
  Chamise (*Adenostoma fasciculatum*)
  Lupines (*Lupinus spp.*)
  Chaparral Pea (*Pickeringia montana*)

Southern Oak Woodlands

Most grasslands plants are common here plus these indicator plants.

* Black Oak   (*Quercus kelloggi*)
* Coast Live Oak (*Q. agrifolia*)
  California Walnut (*Juglans californica*)
* Valley Oak (*Quercus lobata*)
* Interior Live Oak   (*Q. wislizenii*)
  Soft Chess (*Bromus hordeaceus*)
  Red Brome (*B. rubens*)
  Mouse Barley (*Hordeum murinum*)
  Wild Oats (*Avena fatua*)
  Big Quaking Grass (*Briza maxima*)
  Fescues (*Festuca spp.*)
  Western Rye Grass (*Elymus glaucus*)
  Bent Grass (*Agrostis spp.*)
  Poison Oak (*Rhus diversiloba*)
  Fuller's Teasel (*Dipsacus fullonum*)
  Star Thistles (*Centaurea spp.*)
  Curley Dock (*Rumex crispus*)
  Mustards (*Brassica spp.*)
  Narrow-leafed Milkweed (*Asclepias fascicularis*)

The following animals are common in Riparian or Streamside Woodlands and moist Foothill Woodlands.

Insects (No species will be indicated)

* Water Striders (*Gerris spp.*)
* Water Boatman (*Cenocorixa spp.*)
* Back Swimmers (*Notonecta spp.*)
* Giant Water Bugs (*Belostoma spp.*)
  Toad Bugs (*Gelastocoris spp.*)
* Dragon-flies (*Libellula spp.*)
* Damsel-flies (*Argia spp.*)
  May-flies (*Callibaetis spp.*)
  Caddis-flies (*Limnephilus spp.*)
  Dobson-flies (*Corydalus spp.*)
* Predaceous Diving Beetles (*Dytiscidae*)
* Whirligig Beetles (*Gyrinidae*)
  Water Scavengers (*Hydrophilidae*)
  Mosquitos (*Culex spp.*)
* Gnats (*Chironomidae*)
  Black Flies (*Simuliidae*)

Miscellaneous Invertebrates

  Freshwater Hydra (*Hydra spp.*)
  Freshwater Sponges (*Spongilla spp.*)
  Planaria (*Euplanaria spp.*)
  Large Water Snails (*Lymnaea spp.*)
  Small Water Snails (*Physa spp.*)
  Sow Bugs (*Porcellio spp.*)
  Crayfish (*Pacifastacus spp.*)
  Centipedes (*Scolopendra spp.*)
  Millipedes (*Spirobolus spp.*)

The Vertebrates of Moist Woodlands

Fish

* Sticklebacks (*Gasterosteus spp.*)
* Mosquitofish (*Gambusia affinis*)
  Rainbow Trout (*Salmo gairdnerii*)
  Sunfishes (*Lepomis spp.*)

Amphibians

* * Red-legged Frog *(Rana aurora)*
* * Yellow-legged Frog *(R. boylei)*
* * Pacific Tree Frog *(Hyla regilla)*
* * Western Toad *(Bufo boreas)*
* * California Newt *(Taricha torosa)*
* * Arboreal Salamander *(Aneides lugubris)*
* * California Slender Salamander *(Batrachoseps attenuatus)*
  Pacific Giant Salamander *(Dicamptodon ensatus)*
  Tiger Salamander *(Ambystoma tigrinum)*
  Eschscholtz's Salamander *(Ensatina eschscholtzi)*
  Black Salamander *(Aneides flavipunctatus)*

Reptiles

* * Common Garter Snake *(Thamnophis sirtalis)*
* * Western Garter Snake *(T. elegans)*
* * Western Ring-Necked Snake *(Diadophis amabilis)*
* * Rubber Boa *(Charina bottae)*
* * Racers *(Coluber constrictor)*
  Gopher Snake *(Pituophis catenifer)*
  Sharp-Tailed Snake *(Contia tenuis)*
  California Mountain Kingsnake *(Lampropeltis zonata)*
  Western Fence Lizard *(Sceloporus occidentalis)*
  Northern Alligator Lizard *(Gerrhonotus coeruleus)*
  Western Skink *(Eumeces skiltonianus)*
  Western Pond Turtle *(Clemmys marmorata)*

Mammals

* * Western Grey Squirrel *(Sciurus griseus)*
* * Fox Squirrel *(S. niger)*
* * Common Opossum *(Didelphis marsupialis)*
* * Raccoon *(Procyon lotor)*
* * Striped Skunk *(Mephitis mephitis)*
* * Vagrant Shrew *(Sorex vagrans)*
* * Ornate Shrew *(S. ornatus)*
* * Trowbridge Shrew *(S. trowbridgii)*
* * Little Brown Bat *(Myotis lucifugus)*
* * Pallid Bat *(Antrozous pallidus)*
* * Red Bat *(Lasiurus borealis)*

Vertebrates of Moist Woodlands (continued)

Mammals (continued)

* Dusty-Footed Wood Rat (*Neotoma fuscipes*)
* White-Footed Deer Mouse (*Peromyscus maniculatus*)
  Western Harvest Mouse (*Reithrodontomys megalotis*)
  Botta Pocket Gopher (*Thomomys bottae*)
  Beaver (*Castor canadensis*)
  Long-Tailed Weasel (*Mustela frenata*)
  Black Rat (*Rattus rattus*)
  Mule Deer (*Odocoileus hemionus*)
  Bobcat (*Lynx rufus*)
  Muskrat (*Ondatra zibethica*)

Birds

* Green Heron (*Butorides virescens*)
* Black-Crowned Night Heron (*Nycticorax nycticorax*)
* American Bittern (*Botaurus lentiginosus*)
* Wood Ducks (*Aix sponsa*)
  Great Blue Heron (*Ardea herodias*)
  Sparrow Hawk (*Falco sparverius*)
  Cooper's Hawk (*Accipiter cooperii*)
  Red-Shouldered Hawk (*Buteo lineatus*)
  Red-Tailed Hawk (*B. jamaicensis*)
  White-Tailed Kite (*Elanus leucurus*)
* Violet-Green Swallow (*Tachycineta thalassina*)
* Tree Swallow (*Iridoprocne bicolor*)
* Black Phoebe (*Sayornis nigricans*)
* Western Flycatcher (*Empidonax difficilis*)
* Hermit Thrush (*Hylocichla guttata*)
* Robin (*Turdus migratorius*)
* Varied Thrush (*Ixoreus naevius*)
* Brewer Blackbird (*Euphagus cyanocephalus*)
  Red-Winged Blackbird (*Agelaius phoeniceus*)
  Tricolored Blackbird (*A. tricolor*)
* California Valley Quail (*Lophortyx californicus*)
* Song Sparrow (*Melospiza melodia*)
* Greenbacked Goldfinch (*Spinus psaltria*)
* American Goldfinch (*S. tristis*)
* Pileolated Warbler (*Wilsonia pusilla*)

Vertebrates of Moist Woodlands (continued)

Birds (continued)

* Bewick's Wren *(Thryomanes bewickii)*
* House Wren *(Troglodytes aedon)*
* Hutton's Vireo *(Vireo huttoni)*
  Purple Finch *(Carpodacus purpureus)*
  Savanna Sparrow *(Passerculus sandwichensis)*
  Spotted Towhee *(Pipilo erythrophthalmus)*
  Brown Towhee *(P. fuscus)*
  Black Headed Grosbeak *(Pheucticus melanocephalus)*
  Ruby-Crowned Kinglet *(Regulus calendula)*
  Western Bluebird *(Sialia mexicana)*
  Chestnut-Backed Chickadee *(Parus rufescens)*
  Steller Jay *(Cyanocitta stelleri)*
  Western Wood Peewee *(Contopus sordidulus)*
  Red-Shafted Flicker *(Colaptes cafer)*
  Belted Kingfisher *(Megaceryle alcyon)*
  Downy Woodpecker *(Dendrocopos pubescens)*
  Hairy Woodpecker *(D. villosus)*
  Bank Swallow *(Riparia riparia)*
  Black-Chinned Hummingbird *(Archilochus alexandri)*
  Screech Owl *(Otus asio)*
  Long-Eared Owl *(Asio otus)*
  Killdeer *(Charadrius vociferus)*
  Mourning Dove *(Zenaidura macroura)*

The following animals will be more common in the drier Northern and Southern Oak Woodlands. Do not forget that any animal from a nearby biome may also move into these areas.

Amphibians and Reptiles

* Western Toad *(Bufo boreas)*
  Western Spadefoot Toad *(Scaphiopus hammondi)*
  Western Rattlesnake *(Crotalus viridis)*
  Gopher Snake *(Pituophis catenifer)*
  Common Kingsnake *(Lampropeltis getulus)*
  Racer *(Coluber constrictor)*
* Alligator Lizards *(Gerrhonotus spp.)*
  Western Skink *(Eumeces skiltonianus)*

Mammals

Coyote (*Canis latrans*)
Mule Deer (*Odocoileus hemionus*)
Broad-Handed Mole (*Scapanus latimanus*)
Botta Pocket Gopher (*Thomomys bottae*)
* Western Grey Squirrel (*Sciurus griseus*)
California Ground Squirrel (*Otospermophilus beecheyi*)
California Meadow Mouse (*Microtus californicus*)
Black-Tailed Jack Rabbit (*Lepus californicus*)
Rodents (many types)

Birds

Turkey Vulture (*Cathartes aura*)
Sharp-Shinned Hawk (*Accipiter striatus*)
Cooper Hawk (*A. cooperii*)
Sparrow Hawk (*Falco sparveius*)
Barn Owl (*Tyto alba*)
Burrowing Owl (*Speotyto cunicularia*)
Pygmy Owl (*Glaucidium gnoma*)
Band-Tailed Pigeon (*Columba fasciata*)
Mourning Dove (*Zenaidura macroura*)
Acorn Woodpecker (*Melanerpes formicivora*)
Lewis Woodpecker (*Asyndesmus lewis*)
Nuttall Woodpecker (*Dendrocopos nuttallii*)
Red-Shafted Flicker (*Colaptes cafer*)
Crow (*Corvus brachyrhynchos*)
Scrub Jay (*Aphelocoma coerulescens*)
White-Breasted Nuthatch (*Sitta carolinensis*)
Pygmy Nuthatch (*S. pygmaea*)
Creeper (*Certhia familiaris*)
Mockingbird (*Mimus polyglottus*)
Phainopepla (*Phainopepla nitens*)
Audubon Warbler (*Dendroica auduboni*)
Western Tanager (*Piranga ludoviciana*)
Oregon Junco (*Junco oreganus*)
Chipping Sparrow (*Spizella passerina*)
Pine Siskin (*Spinus pinus*)
Yellow Throat (*Geothlypis trichas*)
Bush-Tit (*Psaltriparus minimus*)
Orange-Crowned Warbler (*Vermivora celata*)

Field Exercise #9

Name _____
Score _____

Choose any one type of Broadleaf Forests noted on this trip and list its characteristic plants and animals.

Plants

1.
2.
3.
4.
5.
6.
7.
8.
9.
10.
11.
12.
13.
14.
15.
16.
17.
18.
19.
20.

Animals

Invertebrates

1.
2.
3.
4.
5.
6.
7.
8.
9.
10.
11.
12.
13.
14.
15.

"Herps"

1.
2.
3.
4.
5.
6.
7.
8.
9.
10.

Birds and Mammals

1.
2.
3.
4.
5.
6.
7.
8.
9.
10.
11.
12.
13.
14.
15.
16.
17.
18.
19.
20.

Miner's Lettuce

Trout

Field Exercise #10   Name_____

                                      Score_____

    Discuss how the environmental factors control the amount and type of plant cover which characterizes any one type of Broadleaf Forests.

THE CONIFEROUS, OR FOG BELT, EVERGREEN FORESTS

This type of forest is locally found on tops of the Coastal Ranges from Marin County south into Santa Cruz and Monterey counties. This biome occurs on the western slopes and tops of the Coastal Ranges where the fog brings additional amounts of moisture and precipitation. This precipitation comes not only as rain, but also comes from fog condensing on the leaves (needles) and rough bark and falling as droplets of water. This additional water falls to the ground and trickles into small rivulets and creeks eventually flowing together into streams which flow down from the hills and canyons.

This area has moderately deep soil, more leaf litter and surface organics, is more moist, shady and is generally cooler. These elements combine to produce a dense and beautiful forest filled with picturesque scenes and interesting plants and animals.

Cone forests can be seen along Skyline Road from San Bruno into Santa Cruz. Skyline Road runs through the cone forests generally south of the Half Moon Bay Road. The area described in the chapter fits well for Huddart Park and Portola State Park, both of which are in the southern part of San Mateo County, and for Big Basin Park in Santa Cruz County. Trails and dirt roads may be utilized to discover the plants and animals of this biome.

Besides the true Redwood forests we will also encounter Mixed Evergreen Forests. These green trees may be representatives of any of the Raparian or Broadleaf Forest areas or members of the Chaparral Biome. For descriptions of these plants and animals see the appropriate chapters.

The primary trees in the cone forest are evergreen, softwood trees like the Redwoods, Pines, Cypress and Firs. Another common group of Fog Belt Forest trees are the deciduous Broadleaf Trees that are interdispersed among the evergreens. All these trees are shade resistant and need more moisture.

The Coast Redwood (*Sequoia sempervirens*) is the largest and most characteristic evergreen tree in the coastal fog forest. The redwood has thick, shaggy, fire-resistant bark and flat, dark green, needle-like leaves. These leaves are stiff and arranged in a flat plane along this stem. This tree is also characterized by having a trunk that grows to a very small point. The trunk may grow to more than 250 feet.

215

The cones of this large tree are small, about 3/4 of an inch in diameter, and are found in clusters on the tips of the branches. The cones turn from green to brown as they mature and open.

The primary method of reproduction is not through the cones and seeds, but through asexual structures called "burls." Each burl may grow into a mature redwood tree.

The redwood has one of the shallowest root systems of any large tree. This allows it to prosper in the shallow soil but this same root system also causes many large trees to fall during wind storms.

These are the oldest trees in the county growing as long as 800-1000 years. Along the coast in the southern part of the county these redwoods were some of the most lumbered trees. Virgin stands of these trees are especially found in Memorial Park, Huddart Park, Portola State Park, and also Big Basin Park in northern Santa Cruz County. Other stands of the redwoods can be seen on Cahill ridge and Ox Mountain west of the Crystal Springs lakes.

The Douglas Fir (*Pseudotsuga menziesii*) is the most common evergreen tree in our county. The Douglas Fir grows to over 200 feet in height, has dark brown rough bark, somewhat like the redwood bark, and soft, short, dark green needles born individually on a short stem (see the appendix #2). The 2"-4" female cones hang near the ends of the branches. The male cones are smaller and orangish in color. This tree is the number one source of construction lumber utilized on the West Coast. The fir is used extensively

cone
needle
Redwood

cone
needle
Douglas Fir

in landscaping, and is the major common Christmas Tree. There are several species of birds and mammals
that live in or on the firs and redwoods. These will be mentioned later
in this chapter.

There are large stands of Monterey
Cypress Trees (*Cupressus macrocarpa*)
in this watershed and along the slopes
of the Santa Cruz ranges. The cypress
is described in an earlier chapter. The
road to Half Moon Bay goes through
several stands of cypress trees about
one mile up the hill from the bridge
across the southern end of the reservoir.

Several species of pines are found
in this fog belt forest. The most common one is the Monterey Pine (*Pinus
radiata*) which has already been mentioned in the chapter on the Open Coast.
Some other common pines are the Bishop Pines and the Knobcone Pine. The
Knobcone Pine (*Pinus attenuata*) and
the Bishop Pine (*Pinus muricata*) can
be found in small clumps or single trees
spread throughout the Santa Cruz mountain slopes. The Bishop Pine grows
higher (80 feet as opposed to 50 feet)
and has its gray-green needles in bun-
dles of 2 whereas the Knobcone Pine
has its shiny green needles in bunches
of 3. In both trees the female cones
are woody and are borne in persistent
whorls on the branches. Some of the
older cones are even overgrown by the
trunk as this tree enlarges. The male
cones are smaller, strobilate or scaly,
yellowish to orange and are usually
found at the ends of the branches.

Pines provide lumber for construction, food from their seeds, and medi-
cinal chemicals from their sap or resin.

cone

scales

Monterey Cypress

This gummy resin is called pitch which was used as a healing mixture by the California Indians. Fossilized pitch is known as amber. Many ancient insects are known only from their remains found in amber crystals.

Other local cone types or needle trees are the Firs (*Abies sp.*), Spruce (*Picea sp.*), Cedar (*Libocedrus sp.*) and the Yews (*Taxus sp.* and *Torreya sp.*). Few of these occur in large numbers and therefore will not be discussed. Few of these are native to the peninsula but some have been planted or escaped and have survived. All of these are utilized as ornamentals and grown in many peninsula yards.

Some broadleaf trees common to our fog belt are Tanbark Oak or Tanoak (*Lithocarpus densiflora*), Red Alder (*Alnus rubra*), Madrone (*Arbutus menziesii*) and possibly a few scattered oaks and buckeyes.

The Tanoak (*Lithocarpus densiflora*), which is not a true oak, grows to a tall height (150 feet) competing for light with the firs and redwoods. The bark is very thick, smooth, and is grayish. It is usually partially covered with mosses and/or lichens. This bark is a source of tannin which is a chemical used to tan leather. The evergreen leaves are 2-4 inches long, and have a toothed or spiny margin. The leaves are reddish-green above and fuzzy gray underneath. The flower, a catkin, matures into a plump acorn set in a scaled cup. This acorn is also woolly. These acorns provide food for squirrels and other rodents.

The Red Alder (*Alnus rubra*) is deciduous and like the Tanoak, is a

Tanoak

Red Alder

shade-tolerant tree that can exist in the cool dark areas of cone forests. This tree will grow to 80 feet or more if the soil, moisture and sunlight factors are optimum. The bark is smooth, white or mottled outside and rusty red inside. The leaves grow up to 4" long, are serrated (finely-toothed), and have rolled margins. The leaves are deep green on top and lighter, with protruding veins, underneath. The male flowers are 3" catkins and the female produces small cone-like structures. These deciduous trees often grow in thick stands providing protection and nesting places for small animals.

The Madrone (*Arbutus menziesii*) has leathery, evergreen leaves with finely-toothed margins. The upper surface is dark green while the underside is lighter. The trunk has large patches of reddish-orange bark made apparent by the peeling of the outer bark. The tree grows up to 90 feet high depending on environmental factors. The tiny white bell-like flowers hang in bunches at the ends of the branches. The waxy flowers turn into 1/2 inch reddish berries. These berries provide food for birds and rodents.

Some common shrubs found in the cone forests include the California Huckleberry (*Vaccinium ovatum*) and and the Red Huckleberry (*V. Parvifolium*). Both produce delicious fruits from the small pink flowers which look like manzanita flowers and these fruits are utilized by man and other animals. In both plants the leaves are alternated on the stems, but the California Huckleberry has serrated, 3/4 inch leaves that are dark green and stiff compared to the

Madrone

Huckleberry

Thimbleberry

Gooseberry

Red Flowering Currant

leaves of the Red Huckleberry. The Black Huckleberry is evergreen while the Red Huckleberry is deciduous, losing its leaves in the winter.

Other edible, berry-producing shrubs in the cone forest are thimbleberry, gooseberry, and currants. Thimbleberry (*Rubus parviflorus*) grows to 6 feet in height and has large (3-6 inch) palmately lobed, soft and fuzzy leaves that are serrated and deciduous. The 2-inch white, 5-petaled flowers mature into a soft reddish berry. The stems are gray and the bark shreds and easily peels in older plants. This bush grows in patches, like blackberries, in small sunny clearings or along road cuts and open spaces in the dense forest. This plant, like the other berries, produces food for many small animals.

Gooseberries and currants both belong to the genus Ribes. Of the 17 species of gooseberries in California the most common one in the Bay Area is the Canyon or Common Gooseberry (*Ribes menziesii*). This is a thorny, 6-8 foot shrub with small, 1 1/2 inch lobed leaves. All branches are prickly and have thorns. The white-petaled flowers have red or purple sepals and turn into dark, 1/4 inch purple fruits. The berries or fruits are spiny, thin-skinned, and have many seeds.

The Red Flowering Currant (*Ribes sanguineum*) is another colorful plant that produces edible berries. This plant grows to 10 feet, but unlike the gooseberry, has no thorns on its branches. The bright green leaves are lobed in 5 parts and are about 1 1/2 inches across. The red to pink flowers

mature into small dark blue berries
that attract birds. This plant is very
fragrant and in some areas is called
the "incense-shrub. "

There are 11 species of Ceanothus
or California Lilac found in the area.
Many of these are commonly called
Buck Brush or Deer Brush.

Real Deer Brush (*Ceanothus integerrimus*) is a chaparral species that
creeps into moist areas of the cone
forests. This bush grows to 10 feet
or more, and has deciduous leaves
characterized by having one main vein
and several prominent lateral veins.
The leaves are 1" by 2" in size, have
entire margins and are light green.
The flowers are white or bluish, are
borne in clusters and are very fragrant. This plant, as the name implies, provides much food for deer
and other browsing animals.

Blue Blossum Ceanothus (*C. thyrsiflorus*) is also common in our cone
forests and is very similar to Deer
Brush. The primary difference is its
more narrow leaves and the bluer
flowers.

There are 5 main ferns common to
our cone forests. Each is easy to
identify and can quite readily be col-
lected. One of the largest ferns in the
area is the Western Sword Fern (*Polystichum munitum*) which grows to 5
feet and occurs in large clumps. The
Sword Fern has one main stem covered with brown hair-like scales. Each
stem has many opposite serrated "leaflets. " The fronds (entire stem with its
side leaf-like branches) forms from a
curled structure called a fiddlehead.
The upper side of the fronds is dark

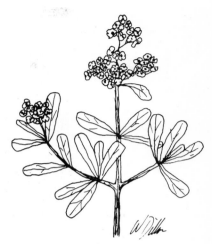

Buck Brush

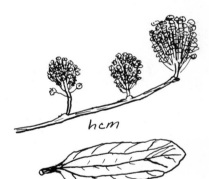

Blue Blossom Ceanothus

Western Sword Fern

Giant Chain Fern

Bracken Fern

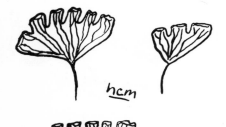

Five-finger Fern

green while the undersurface is lighter and contains round brown dots which are the reproductive conceptacles or sori. The rhizoids or root-like structures grow under the ground, have a brown outer surface and contain the stored food.

The Giant Chain Fern (*Woodwardia fimbriata*) grows as tall as the Sword fern or in ideal conditions may even grow taller. It also has one main stem but the fronds is deeply cleft, almost to the center stem and the leaflets are semi-alternate. The upper surface is lighter and the sori are brown, oblong, and in a chain-like row. This plant was used as a source of red dyes and fibers by the California Indians.

Another tall fern (up to 4 feet) is the Bracken Fern (*Pteridium aquilinum*). It has the fronds with its "leaflets" arranged in a pinnately compound-like pattern. Each side "stem" is alternate in arrangements. The young fronds form from the rhizome as a tiny fiddlehead. The most characteristic feature is the side branching of the main stem. These ferns provide food for deer, small animals, and other herbivores.

Two smaller ferns fairly common to the cone forests are the Five-finger Fern (*Adiantum pedatum*) and the Coastal Wood Ferns (*Dryopteris arguta*); both grow to about 2 - 2 1/2 feet.

The Five-finger Fern has thin, shiny, black stalks. Each stalk has side branches with alternate leaflets. The outer edge of the leaflet is lobed into 5 to 8 curved areas. These outer edges house the curved sori. This plant grows only in cool, damp, protected

rocky areas. The upper surface of
each leaf is a bright, light green and
the undersurface is slightly whiter.
This fern, along with the Chain Fern
and Bracken Fern, can be found in the
cone forests south and west of Huddart
Park. The more common California
Maiden Hair Fern (*Adiantum jordani*)
is also found here.

The Wood Ferns grow up to 30 inches
and are much like the Sword Fern, but
each leaflet also appears to have sub-
leaflets. This fern has roundish-shaped
sori on the underside of the sub-leaf-
lets. The rhizoid (underground stem)
is stout and woody. The lower stems
are covered with brownish scales.

Many mosses and mushrooms are
common in the cone forests but these
organisms are very difficult to identify.
Please note the references.

Parmelia flaventior is a foliose
lichen which is very common in our
cone forests. It is powdery light green
above, blackish below and it grows as
a flat, leaf-like epiphyte on the branches
or trunks of trees and also on rocks.
The undersurface is black. The thallus may grow to 4 or 5 inches long and
2 inches wide but it is only one-eighth
to one-sixteenth of an inch thick.

Another common lichen is the yellowish-green fruticose (thin branching)
Staghorn Lichen (*Letharia vulpina*).
This and other lichens cover the trees
and bushes in moist and foggy areas.

A lichen is a symbiosis (living together) of two different types of plants.
One of the plants is a fungus which is
a non-chlorophyllous plant that provides
the main support, carbon dioxide (CO_2)
and minerals for the other plant. The

Maiden Hair Fern

Bracken Fungi

Gold-back Fern

Foliose Lichen

Staghorn Lichen

Brownies

Western Wake Robin

pores of the fungus also trap water which is used in the metabolism of the other member of the symbiosis which is an algae. The algae produces oxygen, sugars, and other plant chemicals essential for the fungus. Both benefit from the symbiosis.

Many types of beautiful flowers can be found in the cone forest. Most of these are ephemerals and only last for a short time. Because of their large numbers and because of their seasonality only the most obvious, numerous, or interesting will be mentioned. We will try to put them in chronological order starting with the spring flowers.

Some of the earliest flowers to bloom in the cone forest are the Slink Pod, or Brownies (*Scoliopus bigelovii*) and the Western Trillium [Western Wake Robin] (*Trillium ovatum*).

Slink Pod is characterized by having two leaves (rarely three) and the leaves are dark green and spotted with brown or purple as are the flowers. Each leaf may grow 8 to 9 inches long and will have 4 to 6 prominent veins. The leaves are tongue-shaped and have entire margins. The flowers with all their parts (petals, anther, etc.) are in multiples of 3's and are borne as long, thread-like stalks. The flowers have a bad odor and this plant is sometimes called the Fetid Adder's Tongue.

The Western Wake Robin is very common and also is an early bloomer. The flower is white and has three petals. The plant also has three leaves in a whorl pattern. Each leaf is ovate in shape and is usually unmottled. The entire plant is less than one foot tall and grows out of the leaf litter from a rhizoid-like root.

The Redwood Violet (*Viola semper-virens*) is the evergreen, lemon yellow violet most common to our cone forests. This violet has one flower on an erect stem which grows to about 4 inches. The leaves are heart-shaped and have slightly indented margins. This violet reproduces by stolons that creep over the ground and produce new plants at each node.

A taller, larger leaved violet is the Stream Violet (*Viola glabella*). This yellow plant grows to almost a foot tall, has large (3 1/2 inch), serrated, heart-shaped leaves and a long (up to 7 inches) stalk that holds the flowers. The plant grows from horizontal roots along stream banks and shaded slopes in both cone forests and in dense broadleaf forests.

Another common forest plant is Redwood Sorrel (*Oxalis oregana*). This plant has three clover-like leaves, grows to about six inches tall and produces white to lavender flowers. The leaves fold up at night, have a sour taste and are a brilliant green color. The stem is completely underground but the long petiole looks like the stem.

Another plant associated with the Sorrel is Wild Ginger (*Asarum cauda-tum*), a perennial herb with creeping stems and heart-shaped leaves. The pinnately veined leaves grow up to four inches with long petioles and the leaves give off a spicy odor when crushed. The flower consists of three brownish-purple sepals only—(no petals are observed).

A strange plant usually associated with the Wild Ginger is the Giant Horsetail (*Equisetum telmateia*). This plant

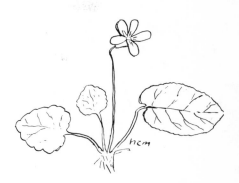

Redwood Violet

— lavender

Redwood Sorrel

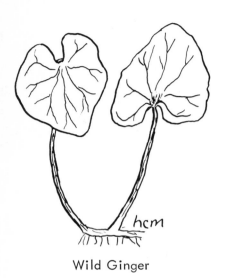

Wild Ginger

Giant Horsetail

grows over three feet tall and the sterile stem is segmented into units. Each unit fits into the one below it and the base of each unit is surrounded by short, pointed projections from the segment below. The stem may be five mm. in diameter and there may be shorter lateral branchlets symmetrically arranged coming from the main stem near the ground. The top of the main stem bears a cone-like strobili which is non-functional. The stem contains a high percentage of silicon and this stem was used by the Indians to clean food utensils and pans. The short, two-inch, fertile stem is short-lived and has a cone (strobili) which produces spores which germinate into whole plants.

The Red Clintonia (*Clintonia andrewsiana*) is a rosy-red, lily-like flower found in the cone forests. It grows to about 18 inches tall and the leaves look somewhat like Brownie leaves but lack the purple spots. The tall flower stalk is leafless and the flowers mature into dark blue berries.

There are two Fairy Bell plants in our cone forests and damp Oak Forests. They are the Fairy Lantern (*Disporum smithii*) and Hooker's Fairy Bell (*D. hookeri*).

The Fairy Lantern grows to 3 feet, has large, 4 inch, oval to heart-shaped leaves with ripply margins and parallel venation. The leaves have no petiole, are alternate in arrangement and they seem to partially overlap the stem. The flowers are yellowish-white and they hang in small clusters under the leaves. Each flower is about 1/2 an inch long and it matures into a dark red berry.

The Fairy Bell is shorter (about 2 feet), has smaller leaves and the leaves have smooth, unrippled margins. The flowers and fruits are similar.

An interesting, long-flowering plant (May to June) found in our cone and mixed forests is the Pacific Starflower (*Trientalis latifolia*). It is more common in shaded and moist areas. The Starflower grows to about 8 inches tall and possesses a whorl of 3 to 6 leaves at the top of its single, thin stem. Each leaf may grow 3 inches long, has a smooth margin and pinnate venation. A small cluster (3-5) of pinkish-red, star-like flowers emerge from the stem where the leaves arise. Each flower is about 1/2 inch in diameter and has six petals and anthers.

Another pretty flower in our cone forests is the Pacific Bleeding Heart (*Dicentra formosa*). Its diagnostic features are the 1 inch, heart-shaped, rose-purple-lavender flowers and its large (1 foot), fern-like leaves. The leaves arise from the stem at ground level, have a long petiole and are compound, being divided into 3 main and many smaller leaflets. The flowers are in clusters which hang from the 1 to 2 foot flower stalk. Each flower has 2 pairs of uneven, overlapping petals that appear heart-shaped and give this flower its name. This plant blooms from April to June.

A pretty little flower that grows in moist soil along stream banks and in the dark shade of the Redwood forest is the Western Wood Anemone (*Anemone quinquefolia*). It never is over 12 inches tall, and it has 3 three-lobed leaves which grow out from the stem.

Red Clintonia

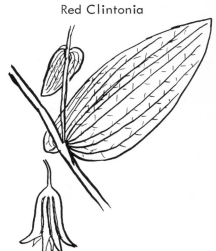

Hooker's Fairy Bell

Pacific Starflower

Western Wood Anemone

Northwestern
Crimson Columbine

Allen's Hummingbird
on a Columbine

Each leaflet is slightly lobed or toothed into 3-5 parts. The single flower is white or light blue, has 5 sepals and blooms from March through May.

A fairly common plant with similar, compound, 3-6 lobed leaves is the Northwestern Crimson Columbine (*Aquilegia formosa*). The columbine grows to 3 feet in height, has dark green leaves and a very characteristic flower. The 5 petals are dark to bright red and fold back from the stamens. Each petal is folded into a long, hollow nectar tube. The stamen and pistils may be golden-yellow in color. This flower blooms later in the year than the Wood Anemone (April through June), and is more often found in mixed cone forests than deep in pure stands of redwoods.

A large leafed plant that grows along streams in the cone forests is the Western Coltsfoot (*Petasites palmatus*), a member of the sunflower family. This stout perennial sends out erect flower stems from creeping root stocks and these stems grow to over 20 inches tall. The white flower is a composite of small flower heads in a disk-like cluster. The stem which holds the flower has small, scale-like leaves. After the flowering stage has passed (March to June), large petioled leaves are produced. Each leaf blade is 5-16 inches wide, is roundish and 7-9 lobed. The leaf is green above and is whitish and somewhat hairy on the undersurface. This plant was used by the Indians as food and by the Europeans to make cough medicine.

Finally we will mention many plants that have been mentioned in the chapters on the Raparian Woodland or the

Broadleaf forest. These plants are
fairly common (like poison oak) and
will often be abundant in many of the
biomes on the peninsula where the environmental conditions permit.

Common moist area plants like the
Miner's Lettuce, Slim Solomon's Seal,
Giant Trillium, Hound's Tongue, Shooting Stars, Yarrow, or Azalea, etc.
have been covered elsewhere in this
book or should already be familiar
plants. These and many other common
plants are used as food sources for
most of the animals that exist in each
area. For references to the many
spring and summer flowers see the list
of books in the reference list.

Azalea

Slender Solomon's Seal

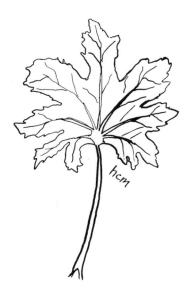

Western Coltsfoot

Hound's Tongue

The animals which inhabit the cone forests, both Redwood and mixed cone, are usually very difficult to observe. They are secretive and most, except the birds, are normally nocturnal. Even the diurnal animals tend to hide or become inactive at the first sign of intruders into their domain. The most numerous, obvious and wary animals in our forests are the birds. These birds have excellent color vision and become aware of any intruder in the forest. Their silence is an indication of danger and most other animals become stilled and hidden. We will discuss the other animals first and end this chapter on the bird life of the cone and mixed forest.

Mule Deer

The largest (in size) animals of the forest are the mammals. The Mule Deer (*Odocoileus hemionus*) is an occasional visitor to the deep forests. At Big Basin and other such parks they are permanent residents of the deep forest, coming to where people will feed them. We have discussed physical characteristics in the chaparral and grasslands where they bed down and feed.

The thousands of deer in San Mateo County will live and be found in all land biomes. They are very adept at hiding quietly in deep grass or under trees and bushes where they normally bed down. They usually return to these rest areas during the heat of each day and only leave this area to feed, drink, mate or when closely approached by some predator or man. They browse on soft grasses and bushes in the early morning and early evenings. Deer will also eat berries, leaves, and flowers when in season. The Mule Deer mate in the early winter after the "rut." During the rutting the dominant males will do battle and will either collect a harem of 2 to 40 females or will be defeated and go unmated that year. The females are each mated and give birth to 1 or 2 fawns by early June. The young suckle until August or September. The fawns are spotted with white dots, but

by early autumn they have molted, after
which they acquire their winter coat
which is thicker and uniform brownish-
gray in color.

The males have antlers which start
their growth along about April. They
are soft and covered with "velvet." By
fall they have grown (they grow larger
each year), and hardened. The males
proceed to rub this velvet off before the
rutting season. The antlers are used
in combat to defeat other males and to
"capture" a harem. The antlers fall
off after the mating season usually by
November or December. In spring
neither sex has antlers, but the male
deer is larger in body size. The cycle
then starts over again. All deer have
cloven hooves which leave a very characteristic track. These tracks are
more obvious than the deer in most
cases. The abundance of these deer
can be estimated by the number killed
on our roads. More than 50 deer a
year are killed on Skyline and LaCanada
Road alone. The authors have seen
herds of more than a hundred in one
afternoon back in the chaparral.

The next smaller animal is the Cougar (*Felis concolor*) which is the primary predator on the deer. The Cougar
or Mountain Lion is found in almost
every county of the state, but because
of their shyness and nocturnal behavior
they are seldom seen. The total range
of this animal is from San Luis Potosí
in Mexico to Northern Canada and
Alaska. They are found in large numbers in California, especially in Monterey County. These animals are known
to travel long distances. This tawny
animal is the largest of the cat family

Black-tailed Deer

Cougar

Bobcat

Coyote

Raccoon

found in North America. The only evidence of this animal to be seen will be the tracks or the remains of a deer killed. Although the main diet of the cougar is deer (25-30 a year), they still take small animals including birds, rodents, skunks, and even dogs. As is true for all animals and plants, the worst enemy of these beautiful animals is man. The cougar mates in the fall and the young (2-4) are born in the spring. The den is usually a cave, crevice or log pile which is often very protected.

Another large (up to 30 inches in length), secretive animal is the Bobcat (*Lynx rufus*). This animal seldom enters the true cone forest, but is found more often in the mixed forest or in the chaparral. The bobcat is much like the cougar in breeding habits, number of young and den selection. The animal is characterized by its short tail, tufted ears, and spotted coat. Unlike the cougar, the bobcat feeds totally on small animals and is a good rodent-control animal. The diet of the bobcat consists of disease-carrying rodents, gophers, meadow mice, ground squirrels, rabbits, and small birds. This animal, like the cougar and coyote, should never be harmed.

Another rodent-control animal occasionally seen in the cone or mixed forest is the Coyote (*Canis latrans*). This animal, like the Grey Fox may stray into the forest to hunt or hide. Since both of these mammals have been mentioned in other chapters, they will not be discussed here.

Three other animals common to the forests are the raccoon, skunk, and

opossum. All three have been discussed previously. These are some of
the more obvious mammals that camp-
ers will note at twilight and dawn. The
state parks in San Mateo County are
commonly invaded by these animals
seeking food. None are dangerous, and
none should be injured nor should you
try to feed these animals by hand. They
are wild and will bite.

Striped Skunk

Another active carnivore in the forest area is the Long-tailed Weasel
(*Mustela frenata*). This 10 to 12 inch
carnivore has reddish-brown fur on its
back and sides and is white to yellowish
on its undersurface. The 5 inch tail
has a black tip. This hunter will be
active both day and night, depending
upon the activity of its prey. The primary food taken by the weasel is small
mammals such as rodents, gophers,
baby rabbits, and an occasional bird.
The weasel uses stealth, cunning, and
speed to capture its prey. It may even
climb trees to get its food. The weasel
also is a den-liver and its litter of 4-6
is born in April and May. By June or
July they are fully grown and have left
the nest to live on their own.

Opossum

The smallest mammalian carnivores
in our county are the shrews. Three
different shrews are endemic to the San
Francisco Peninsula. The Trowbridge
Shrew has been previously mentioned
and will be found in the forest areas.
The other two secretive shrews are
the Adorned Shrew (*Sorex ornatus*) and
the Vagrant Shrew (*S. vagrans*). Both
are exceedingly small, less than 4
inches (tail included), and have a very
pointed muzzle with many stiff whiskers growing on it. They will be found

Ring-tailed Cat

Long-tailed Weasel

Fox Squirrel

Grey Squirrel

Beechey Ground Squirrel

living in moist areas with their dens built in old, decayed, fallen logs or in the soil and leaf litter under these logs. The Adorned Shrew has sooty brown fur on its back. This fur may appear "frosted" due to the longer, silver-tipped hair sprinkled throughout. The belly fur is smoky gray and the tail has a dark tip.

The Vagrant Shrew is reddish-brown above and light, whitish-gray below. The tail appears to have its distal one-half darker in color.

The shrews are the least studied of our local mammals. They are also the least "seen" due to their very secretive nature and because they are mistaken for small mice. The authors have taken shrews from decayed logs in moist forest areas in the county. These shrews feed upon insects, worms, trapped mice, and an occasional plant. They must eat every few hours or they will die from "hunger." Their small body size and relatively large surface area causes them to lose much body heat, hence their high metabolism. Few animals feed on shrews due to their secretive nature, small size, and musky odor.

A few other interesting mammals are found in our cone forests and mixed forests and their grassy clearings. Most have already been mentioned in previous chapters. The more common ones are the Squirrels, both Fox and Grey, and the Beechey Ground Squirrel. Other rodents such as the White-footed Deer Mouse, the Western Harvest Mouse, the Dusky-footed Wood Rat, Pocket Gophers, Moles, and some Bats are also residents of these areas.

Of the 24 species of bats common to California, at least 5 species are generally found in the cone forests of the San Francisco Peninsula. The bats, like the shrews, are very hard to identify and can be identified accurately only by use of the skull and entire animal. Also because of the crepuscular behavioral patterns (dawn and dusk activity) they are rarely seen. Some bats are tree dwellers: for example the Silver-haired Bat (*Lasionycteris noctivagans*), the Hoary Bat (*Lasiurus cinereus*), and the Red Bat (*L. borealis*).

The Hairy-winged Myotis (*Myotis volans*) and the Long-eared Myotis (*Myotis evotis*) are common to our county and forests and are "cave dwellers." They can also be found in any dark, protected place where they may hang in security. Such man-made areas are old buildings, churches, towers, barns, drain pipes, and under road culverts. Since bats are primarily insect eaters they are relatively harmless except that they may carry rabies. If you find a dead bat it should never be picked up by hand but should be carefully removed and/or the county health agency should be called.

The feeding behavior of bats is characterized by their flitting across forest clearings and capturing moths and other insects, while both are in flight. They use their high frequency squeaks (25,000 - 75,000 vibrations per second) to echo locate the prey. They also use their squeaks to avoid flying into objects. The squeaks come from their vocal cords and the returned sound waves are picked up by the bats' ears and these intercepted sound waves

Douglas Squirrel

Flying Squirrel

Red Bat

give the size, direction, and speed of flight of the food object.

There is no one reptile which is found only in the cone forests. Every representative of these groups can be found in most of the other land biomes in the county. A few like the skink will be in moist or forested areas, as will the aquatic forms of the garter snakes and the Common Kingsnake. The most common and obvious reptiles will be the Western Fence Lizard (*Sceloporus occidentalis*) and the Alligator Lizards. Most reptiles eat insects, other reptiles, and amphibians, but some, like the larger snakes, are mammal and bird eaters.

Hairy-winged Bat

The Western Fence Lizard, or Bluebelly, is often seen in the forest areas sitting on logs or rocks "warming up" or sunning itself so it may feed and be active. Each Bluebelly establishes a territory which it defends from other male Fence Lizards by bluff and actual combat. The bluff posture resembles push-ups showing the blue side markings. The male does this in view of other male intruders. In fighting they bite any part of the body in order to drive away other males.

Fence Lizards mate and the eggs are laid from May through July. The 10-15, small (1/4"-1/2") eggs are put in small pits in damp soil where they hatch by August or September. The Fence Lizards feed primarily upon all types of insects, their larvae, spiders, and will, if hungry, even eat their own young.

Western Fence Lizard

The Western Skink (*Eumeces skiltonianus*) is characterized by the bright blue tail. The brown body has lighter stripes in the young. The adults have less blue on their tails and the body stripes become less brilliant. This skink will grow to about 6 inches long and is active in the leaf litter of the forest looking for beetles, spiders, sow bugs, and insect larvae.

A characteristic feature of most of the lizards, but especially so in the skink, is their ability to shed the tail. If roughly handled the vertebrae, blood vessels and muscles will fracture and the tail will drop off and wiggle violently. This is possibly a protective adaptation to draw attention to the tail while the rest of the animal sneaks away. The animal then proceeds to grow a new tail. We actually had an alligator lizard that grew 2 tails after such an injury.

The Southern Alligator Lizard (*Gerrhonotus multicarinatus*) is the more common of the alligator lizards, but the Northern Alligator Lizard (*G. coeruleus*) may also be encountered. These lizards are characterized by a lateral fold which runs between the front and hind legs. We have captured these lizards as much as 15" long (total length). They are normally less than 10" long. The primary difference between these two lizards is in the coloration. The Southern variety is reddish and black while the Northern Lizard is yellowish and black. Both eat insects, spiders, larvae of many types and even an occasional millipede or snail.

The rest of the reptiles to be encountered are the snakes. These animals are active at lower temperatures than the lizards and other cold-blooded animals on which they feed.

Skink

Northern Alligator Lizard

Some of the snakes already mentioned will not be elaborated upon in this cahpter. These are the Gopher Snake, Common Kingsnake, Racers, and the Ring-necked Snake, all of which will be encountered in the grassy clearings and along the edges of the forests and in the leafy areas under the trees.

One rare and secretive snake found in the forested areas is the Sharp-tailed Snake (*Contia tenuis*). This snake rarely grows over one foot in length and is easily identified by three features. The body is gray above and has black cross bars on the undersurface. This snake has a sharp spine at the tip of the tail, but the function of this spine is unknown. Finally, this snake has many long teeth and it feeds almost entirely upon slugs. The Sharp-tail lives underground, in leaf litter, in rotten logs, and under rocks. It is more common in moist areas and after rains when its food is more abundant.

A much more common snake in the forests is the Western Garter Snake (*Thamnophis elegans*), both the aquatic and land type. Both types grow to 3 feet in length and the primary visible difference is that the aquatic type is gray with a dorsal yellow stripe running the length of the body while the land variety is mottled red and black, but it also has a dorsal yellow stripe running the length of the body. In both types the female retains the eggs (4-12 in number) inside her body and at birth the young are only covered by a clear membrane which immediately breaks when the young "hatch." The food preference of the Western Garter Snake is very wide. The land type will

Sharp-tailed Snake

aquatic

land-dwelling

Western Garter Snake

eat any smaller reptile or amphibian, as well as mice, birds, insects, worms, slugs, or even small rabbits. The aquatic variety will eat more frogs, tadpoles, fish, and salamanders.

Some of the more common animals of the moist cone forests are the amphibians. Due to the foggy weather, water condensation and rains which are prevalent to that area we would expect a larger occurrence of the wet-skinned organisms. The "extra" water also allows for small permanent ponds, continuous running streams, and an occasional lake. This area along with the Raparian Woodlands have the largest number of different types of amphibians, because the amphibians must lay their eggs either in water or where it is extremely moist. The additional moisture also allows for a large number of aquatic insects, both larvae and adults. These insects can breed and lay their eggs in small pockets of water, in hollows of trees, in small rocky ponds, and in moist leaf litter or in the available streams.

One of the larger amphibians of the permanent streams and moist streamside woodlands of the peninsula's cone forest is the Pacific Giant Salamander (*Dicamptodon ensatus*). This animal reaches a total length of just under 12 inches. The body is thick and brown to dark purple with black blotches. There is a segmentation of the muscles in the body wall which results in riblike markings on the sides of the animal. The tail is bigger and blade-like for more efficient swimming. The larvae and adults may be found in streams at any time of the year, but

Pacific Giant Salamander

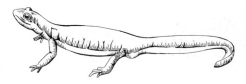

California Newt

most eggs are laid in the spring, and they hatch by September. These are more active predators than most amphibians and the larvae feed on aquatic insects and dead animals in the stream while the adults eat insects, small snails, and slugs, and will also take other smaller salamanders, frogs, snakes, and even an occasional rodent.

Our cone forests contain both species of the newts. The California Newt (*Taricha torosa*) was mentioned in the chapter on the Raparian Woodlands. That animal is more common in our streams, lakes, and moist areas, but the Rough-skinned Newt (*T. granulosa*) can occasionally be found in or near streams and lakes. The Rough-skinned Newt is brown above and yellowish to orange on its undersurface. It is about the same size as the California Newt (6 to 7 inches). The primary differences are that the brown coloration goes completely under the eye, and the eyes do not project over the jaws when viewed from above.

Both newts breed in the winter (wet season) and after their courtship, the eggs are laid in clusters hooked to logs and weeds in the water. The eggs hatch in about 5 weeks into tadpole-like larvae. These larvae will eat insect larvae such as mosquito, wigglers, and also water plants and other organic debris. When the larvae change into the adult form they change their diet so that worms, snails, slugs, and insect larvae and adults are the main foods. The newts, like most other amphibians, provide food for the raccoons, snakes, predaceous birds, and large toads and frogs.

Rough-skinned Newt

Tiger Salamander

Another fairly common, although secretive, salamander is the Orange or Eschscholtz Salamander (*Ensatina eschscholtzi*). This 3-4 inch salamander is easy to identify. It is orange in color with a whitish belly and the tail is very narrow at its base. The skin is smooth and has the same type of segmentation as found in the Pacific Giant Salamander and the Arboreal Salamander. These animals are found in moist forest areas, near, but not in streams, and in the leaf litter or under rocks, and logs. The Ensatina mate, often after an elaborate courtship, in a manner similar to the newts. The mating takes place in the late fall or early winter. The eggs are laid in the spring and they hatch in the late summer to early fall. The Ensatina have a typical diet of insects, ground "bugs", worms, and centipedes.

California Slender Salamander

Arboreal Salamander

Several salamanders may be encountered in the cone forests, its clearings or its borders with other biomes. These animals have been mentioned in the appropriate chapters, but we will mention the most likely ones which a person might find. They are the Tiger Salamander (*Ambystoma tigrinum*), the California Slender Salamander (*Batrachoseps attenuatus*), the Arboreal Salamander (*Aneides lugubris*), and the Black Salamander (*A. flavipunctatus*). All of these animals lay their eggs in water or moist areas, generally eat (in the adult forms) insects, centipedes, sow bugs, snails, and worms and, in turn, the salamanders provide food for many predators such as birds, mammals, and snakes.

Black Salamander

Green or Pacific Tree Frog

Red-legged Frog

Yellow-legged Frog

Two other amphibians are common to the cone forests. Both animals have been mentioned in other chapters. These are the Pacific Tree Frog (*Hyla regilla*) and the Red-legged Frog (*Rana aurora*). Both need water in which to lay their eggs and to allow the growth and feeding of the tadpoles. The tadpoles eat algae and other plant debris that falls in the water. The "tads" breathe from exposed gills, and after a few weeks (the time is variable depending upon food and temperature), they change into the adult form. The adult frogs feed upon insects and other small animals, breathe by lungs and skin, if it is moist enough, and may leave the water. These animals must return to the water to lay their jelly-coated eggs. The adults also make noise, that is, the males do for only the males have vocal pouches. The females remain silent, but respond to the mating call.

The most numerous, large animals found in our cone forests are the birds. More than a hundred species of birds could be listed as being common to the county's forests. Many are residents, some are annual migrants, a few are rare visitors. Due to their rapid and easy mobility, many birds, more common to other biomes, may also occasionally be encountered. These birds are very important elements in the ecology of the peninsula. Some are insect-control agents, others are rodent-control factors, some are harmful to man or his belongings, but all are interesting and usually very beautiful.

Birds have excellent sight and are usually the first to know of the presence of intruders to their areas. This

ability allows them to remain silent
or swiftly escape detection by flying
away. We will attempt to describe
and discuss only the more common,
important, or interesting birds of this
area, not every bird. Some of the
most interesting of the birds are the
large predators such as the eagles,
hawks, and owls.

The only eagle found in the area is
the Golden Eagle (*Aquila chrysaetos*).
The Golden Eagles are large (having
a body length of almost 3 feet and a
wingspread of more than 6 feet), are
uniformly dark brown and have large
heads, necks, and bills. The head is
"golden" in color. The young have
white feathers on their tails and white
wing patches.

Golden Eagle

Each pair of birds has a large territory of some 20-30 square miles, in
which they build a large nest (aerie) of
sticks in a tree or more commonly on
a cliff. These birds utilize tree nests
in San Mateo and Santa Cruz counties.
These eagles capture mammals such
as rabbits, squirrels, an occasional
sheep, and many birds such as ducks,
coots, quails, and sometimes a chicken.
These eagles also eat much carrion.
The eagles should be considered as
beneficial animals and are protected
by Federal Law.

A very small hawk (body length 10-
12 inches, wingspread about 2 feet) is
the Sharp-shinned Hawk (*Accipiter
striatus*). This hawk has a long, square
or slightly notched, tail with a black
underband and short, rounded wings.
The adults have gray backs and a rusty-
barred breast. Its flight is characteristically a few quick beats followed by

Sharp-skinned Hawk

a gliding sequence. This hawk hunts
like the other members of the same
genus. It will fly close to the ground,
using its characteristic flight pattern,
until it surprises its prey. Then it
will drop directly upon the animal. If
it misses the "kill" it may chase the
prey (if a mammal) a short distance
upon foot. If the prey is a bird, the
Sharp-shin will follow the intended victim with much maneuvering until the
"kill." These hawks feed primarily
upon small birds such as sparrows,
warblers, pigeons, or quail, and small
mammals such as squirrels, mice, or
shrews. This hawk builds its nest o
sticks and twigs high in the conifers
The eggs are few in number (4-6) and
are spotted with brown.

Cooper's Hawk

Another hawk similar in appearance to the Sharp-shinned Hawk is the
Cooper's Hawk (*Accipiter cooperii*)
The Cooper's Hawk is larger in size
(16 inches in body length and a 28-30
inch wingspan) than the Sharp-shinned
Hawk, but has about the same color
pattern. The adult male has a gray
back, rusty red breast, dark bands or
the tail, but the Cooper's Hawk lack
the notched tail of the Sharp-shinne
Hawk. The immature Cooper's Hawk
have brownish back feathers and hav
a brown streaked breast as do the im
mature Sharp-shinned Hawks.

Red-tailed Hawk

The Cooper's Hawks look and be
have exactly like the Sharp-shinne
Hawks, and they even fly like them
The food of the Cooper's Hawk is sim
ilar, but it may take more slightl
larger birds and mammals and eve
an occasional chicken. The Cooper'
Hawk nests in conifers and the nest i

a large, flat platform of sticks and twigs.

Another common hawk is the Red-tailed Hawk (*Buteo jamaicensis*) which has been mentioned in several other chapters. This hawk may be seen sitting in trees along the forest edges.

Several owls are common to cone forests. One that was already mentioned was the Great Horned Owl (*Bubo virginianus*). This large bird, body length 18 inches and wingspan 25 inches, builds its nest in cone trees, on the ground or even on cliffs in secluded areas. This large nocturnal predator usually feeds in the savanna or chaparral where it takes rodents (rats, mice, gophers) and rabbits. This owl spits up "pellets" of hair and bones which it cannot digest. These pellets usually mark the presence of their nest site. The Great Horned Owl has the typical deep "hoo-hoo" call of most owls.

Two small owls are common to our cone forest. They are the common Screech Owl (*Otus asio*) and the slightly larger, but more rare, Spotted Owl (*Strix occidentalis*).

The Screech Owl stands 8-10 inches tall and is dark gray and is the one small owl with small "ear tufts." The eyes are large and yellow. These small owls nest in hollows of trees, emerging at night to forage for small rodents and insects.

The Spotted Owl is larger (18 inches total length), has a round head with no ear tufts and it has dark eyes. The feathers are dark brown and there are rows of white spots crossing the chest or front area. These birds also nest

LAWRENCE CARSON

Great Horned Owl

Screech Owl

Spotted Owl

in tree hollows and forage at dusk.
Their primary foods are rodents (wood
rats, white-footed mice), and some
larger insects.

Another active, early evening bird
is the Vaux's Swift (*Chaetura vauxi*).
The small, 4-5 inch, swallow-like bird
has a short blunt body and long, slightly
curved wings. This bird looks like it
lacks a tail. The body is dark brownish-gray above, dingy below and there
is a lighter throat patch. The nest is
a few twigs glued inside a hollow pine,
fir, or redwood tree. These birds
sway high in the air, capturing insects
with bat-like maneuvers.

Besides the owls, swift and possibly
a stray poor-will, few birds are active after the early evening and even
the swifts nest at night.

The remainder of the cone forest
birds are smaller and active only from

Vaux's Swift

Band-tail Pigeon

dawn to dusk. Almost any bird from neighboring biomes can be encountered in this area. A few birds which have not been mentioned before, and which are fairly common will now be discussed.

Two birds common in the cone forests are the Band-tail Pigeon and the Steller's Jay. The Band-tail Pigeon (*Columba fasciata*) has a 15 inch wingspan. It is blue-gray in color above with a purplish head and chest. It also has a white stripe on the nape of the neck and a light band near the tip of the tail. The bill and feet are yellow. These birds travel in large flocks and feed upon acorns, and other plants, plus some insects and spiders. These birds provide good sport for the hunter because of their large numbers and rapid flight.

California Scrub Jay

Downy Woodpecker

Steller's Jay

Oregon Junco

The Steller's Jay (*Cyanocitta stelleri*) is a large, robin-sized bird. It has a blue body and a black crested head. This bird is the noisemaker of the cone forest along with the California Scrub Jay (*Aphelocoma californica*) which often strays into this biome. These jays eat acorns, insects and berries.

Woodpeckers are also common in these forests searching for insects on the trunks and limbs of the trees. These can more often be heard "tapping", than seen. These birds also eat pine nuts, berries, spiders and other small foods.

Our smallest woodpecker is the Downy Woodpecker (*Dendrocopos pubescens*). It is the size of a sparrow, is black and white, with a white back and a red spot on the head. The Hairy Woodpecker (*D. villosus*) is larger, is black and white with a cap. This bird has a longer bill.

Creeper

Nuthatch

Flycatcher

The Oregon Junco (*Junco oreganus*) is a sparrow-sized bird with a black head and neck. This seed eater, along with the Spotted Towhee (*Pipilo erythrophthalmus*), which is much larger, are very common. The towhee also has a black head and neck but with its robin size it can be easily distinguished from the junco.

The Brown Creeper (*Certhia familiaris*) is the only small brown bird with a down-curved bill in the cone forests. This insect-eater flits from tree to tree hunting food.

Several flycatchers inhabit the cone forests. All are sparrow-sized, have very pointed bills and sit on exposed limbs waiting for their insect food to fly by. They will dart out, snatch the insect on the wing and return to their perch.

Many smaller birds are common, but secretive in the cone forests. Please note the check list and the reference books for more details.

Hermit Thrush

Chickadee

Ruby-crowned Kinglet

Blue Grosbeck

Male Willow

Wild Rose

Western Azalea

A Check List of Cone Forest Plants and Animals

Those with the asterisks are mentioned in this chapter.

Plants

* Coast Redwood (*Sequoia sempervirens*)
* Douglas Fir (*Pseudotsuga menziesii*)
* Monterey Cypress (*Cupressus macrocarpa*)
* Monterey Pine (*Pinus radiata*)
* Knobcone Pine (*P. attenuata*)
* Bishop Pine (*P. muricata*)
* Spruce (*Picea spp.*)
* Grand Fir (*Abies grandis*)
* Incense Cedar (*Libocedrus decurrens*)
* Western Yew (*Taxus brevifolia*)
* California Nutmeg (*Torreya californica*)
* Tanoak (*Lithocarpus densiflora*)
* Red Alder (*Alnus rubra*)
* Madrone (*Arbutus menziesii*)
* California Huckleberry (*Vaccinium ovatum*)
* Red Huckleberry (*V. parvifolium*)
* Thimbleberry (*Rubus parviflorus*)
  Western Azalea (*Rhododendron occidentale*)
  Coast Barberry (*Berberis pinnata*; [*Mahonia*])
* Canyon Gooseberry (*Ribes menziesii*)
* Red Flowering Currant (*R. sanguineum*)
* Deer Brush (*Ceanothus integerrimus*)
* Blue Blossom (*C. thyrsiflorus*)
* Western Sword Fern (*Polystichum munitum*)
* Giant Chain Fern (*Woodwardia fimbriata*)
  Licorice Fern (*Polypodium glycyrrhiza*)
  Goldenback Fern (*Pityrogramma triangularis*)
* Coastal Wood Fern (*Dryopteris arguta*)
* Bracken Fern (*Pteridium aquilinum*)
* Maidenhair Fern (*Adiantum jordani*)
* Five-finger Fern (*A. pedatum*)
* Foliose Lichen (*Parmelia flaventior*)
* Staghorn Lichen (*Letharia vulpina*)
  Poison Oak (*Rhus diversiloba*)
  Hairy Manzanita (*Arctostaphylos columbiana*)
* Slink Pod (*Scoliopus bigelovii*)

Plants (continued)

* Western Trillium (*Trillium ovatum*)
* Redwood Violet (*Viola sempervirens*)
* Stream Violet (*V. glabella*)
* Redwood Sorrel (*Oxalis oregana*)
* Wild Ginger (*Asarum caudatum*)
* Giant Horsetail (*Equisetum telmateia*)
* Red Clintonia (*Clintonia andrewsiana*)
* Fairy Lantern (*Disporum smithii*)
* Fairy Bell (*D. hookeri*)
* Pacific Starflower (*Trientalis latifolia*)
* Pacific Bleeding Heart (*Dicentra formosa*)
* Western Wood Anemone (*Anemone quinquefolia*)
* Northwestern Crimson Columbine (*Aquilegia formosa*)
* Western Coltsfoot (*Petasites palmatus*)
  Miner's Lettuce (*Montia perfoliata*)
  Slim Solomon's Seal (*Smilacina stellata*)
  Giant Trillium (*Trillium chloropetalum*)
  Hound's Tongue (*Cynoglossum grande*)
  Yarrow (*Achillea millefolium*)
  Red Larkspur (*Delphinium nudicaule*)
  Wood Strawberry (*Fragaria californica*)
  Mist Maiden (*Romanzoffia suksdorfii*)
  Yerba Buena (*Satureja douglasii*)
  Common Monkey Flower (*Mimulus guttatus*)
  Wild Cucumber (*Marah fabaceus*)
  Woodland Madia (*Madia madioides*)
  Ground Iris (*Iris macrosiphon*)
  Stream Orchid (*Epipactis gigantea*)
  French Broom (*Cytisus monspessulanus*)

Mammals

* Mule Deer (*Odocoileus hemionus*)
* Cougar (*Felis concolor*)
* Bobcat (*Lynx rufus*)
* Coyote (*Canis latrans*)
* Long-tailed Weasel (*Mustela frenata*)
  Raccoon (*Procyon lotor*)
  Opossum (*Didelphis marsupialis*)
  Striped Skunk (*Mephitis mephitis*)

Mammals (continued)

*   Adorned Shrew (*Sorex ornatus*)
*   Vagrant Shrew (*S. vagrans*
    Grey Squirrel (*Sciurus griseus*)
    Fox Squirrel (*S. niger*)
    Beechy Ground Squirrel (*Otospermophilus beecheyi*)
    Douglas Squirrel (*Tamiasciurus douglasii*)
    Flying Squirrel (*Glaucomys sabrinus*)
    White-footed Deer Mouse (*Peromyscus maniculatus*)
    Dusky-footed Wood Rat (*Neotoma fuscipes*)
    Pocket Gopher (*Thomomys bottae*)
    Broad-handed Mole (*Scapanus latimanus*)
    Merriam Chipmunk (*Eutamias merriami*)
*   Silver-haired Bat (*Lasionycteris noctivagans*)
*   Hoary Bat (*Lasiurus cinereus*)
*   Red Bat (*L. borealis*)
*   Hairy-winged Myotis (*Myotis volans*)
*   Long-eared Myotis (*M. evotis*)

Reptiles

*   Western Fence Lizard (*Sceloporus occidentalis*)
*   Western Skink (*Eumeces skiltonianus*)
*   Southern Alligator Lizard (*Gerrhonotus multicarinatus*)
*   Northern Alligator Lizard (*G. coeruleus*)
    Gopher Snake (*Pituophis catenifer*)
    Ring-necked Snake (*Diadophis amabilis*)
    Common Kingsnake (*Lampropeltis getulus*)
*   Sharp-tailed Snake (*Contia tenuis*)
*   Western Garter Snake (*Thamnophis elegans*)

Amphibians

*   Pacific Giant Salamander (*Dicamptodon ensatus*)
*   California Newt (*Taricha torosa*)
*   Rough-skinned Newt (*T. granulosa*)
*   Orange Ensatina (*Ensatina eschscholtzi*)
*   Tiger Salamander (*Ambystoma tigrinum*)
*   California Slender Salamander (*Batrachoseps attenuatus*)
*   Arboreal Salamander (*Aneides lugubris*)
*   Black Salamander (*A. flavipunctatus*)

Amphibians (continued)

* Pacific Tree Frog (*Hyla regilla*)
* Red-legged Frog (*Rana aurora*)

Birds

* Golden Eagle (*Aquila chrysaetos*)
* Sharp-shinned Hawk (*Accipiter striatus*)
* Cooper's Hawk (*A. cooperii*)
* Red-tailed Hawk (*Buteo jamaicensis*)
* Great Horned Owl (*Bubo virginianus*)
* Screech Owl (*Otus asio*)
* Spotted Owl (*Strix occidentalis*)
* Vaux's Swift (*Chaetura vauxi*)
* Band-tail Pigeon (*Columba fasciata*)
* Steller's Jay (*Cyanocitta stelleri*)
* Scrub Jay (*Aphelocoma coerulescens*)
* Downy Woodpecker (*Dendrocopos pubescens*)
* Hairy Woodpecker (*D. villosus*)
* Oregon Junco (*Junco oreganus*)
* Spotted Towhee (*Pipilo erythrophthalmus*)
* Brown Creeper (*Certhia familiaris*)
  Olive-sided Flycatcher (*Nuttallornis borealis*)
  Western Flycatcher (*Empidonax difficilis*)
  Purple Martin (*Progne subis*)
  Chestnut-backed Chickadee (*Parus rufescens*)
  Red-breasted Nuthatch (*Sitta canadensis*)
  Varied Thrush (*Ixoreus naevius*)
  Hermit Thrush (*Hylocichla guttata*)
  Kinglets (*Regulus spp.*)
  Warblers (*Dendroica spp.*)
  Western Tanager (*Piranga ludoviciana*)
  Black-headed Grosbeak (*Pheucticus melanocephalus*)
  Purple Finch (*Carpodacus purpureus*)
  Chipping Sparrow (*Spizella passerina*)
  Fox Sparrow (*Passerella iliaca*)

Field Exercise #11

Name _____

Score _____

List the common plants noted and identified during the Cone Forest field trip.

1.   11.

2.   12.

3.   13.

4.   14.

5.   15.

6.   16.

7.   17.

8.   18.

9.   19.

10.   20.

List the animals seen on this trip.

Invertebrates   "Herps"   Birds and Mammals

1.   1.   1.

2.   2.   2.

3.   3.   3.

4.   4.   4.

5.   5.   5.

6.   6.

7.   7.

8.   8.

9.   9.

10.   10.

Field Exercise #12   Name_____

                                      Score_____

    Discuss the unique "weather positioning" effect which in part determines the location of Cone Forests.

Appendix #1

GLOSSARY OF BROAD LEAF TERMS

I. Leaf Types

A. Simple— one leaf blade per petiole. Example: Maple, Elm,
Oak.

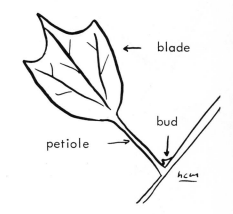

B. Compound—more than one leaf
blade per petiole.

1. Pinnately compound—leaflets or blades arranged
feather-like along the petiole.

a. Singlely pinnately compound—each leaflet or
blade coming from the
main petiole vein com-
plete. Example: Ash,
Pepper, Walnut, Rose.

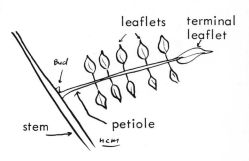

b. Doubly pinnately com-
pound— each leaflet
again divided into sec-
ondary leaflets along
the secondary or lateral
veins. Example: Silver
Acacia, Albizzia.

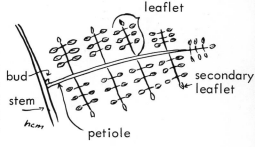

259

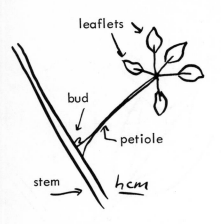

2. Palmately compound—leaflets arranged in a palmlike structure radiating outward from a common center. Example: Lupine, Buckeye.

II. Leaf Arrangement on Stem

A. Alternate—leaves arranged in step-like fashion along either side of stem. Example: Sycamore, Elm, Rose.

B. Opposite—leaves arranged in ladder-like fashion along stem. Example: Maple.

C. Whorled—leaves growing out of stem in all directions from same terminus. Example: Veronica.

III. Blade Types

A. Entire—the edge of blade <u>not</u> deeply indented. Example: Elm, Poplar.

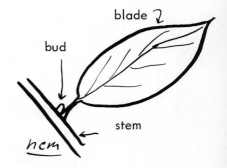

B. Lobed—the edge of blade <u>is</u> deeply indented. Example: Maple, Sycamore.

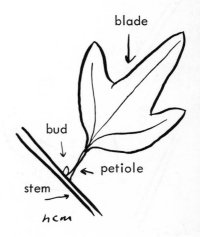

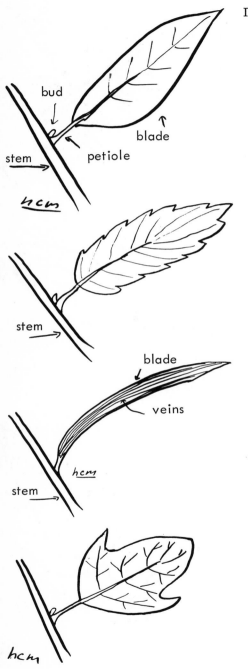

IV. Blade—Edge Types

    A. Smooth—the edge of blade is
       smooth and does not have saw-
       toothed appearance. Example:
       California Bay Laurel, Euca-
       lyptus.

    B. Serrated—the edge of blade is
       not smooth, being either saw-
       toothed or spiked. Example:
       Rose, Elm, Sycamore.

V. Vein Types

    A. Parallel—all major veins run-
       ning full length of blade from
       petiole to terminus. Example:
       Grass, Iris, Bamboo, Palms.

    B. Net—all major veins not run-
       ning full length of blade, veins
       not straight. Example: Ma-
       ple, Elm, Rose.

1. Pinnate-net. Secondary veins running laterally from main petiole vein. Example: Elm, Coffee Berry.

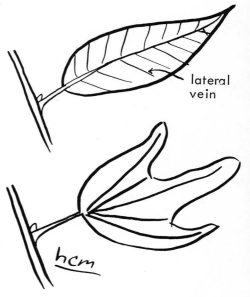

lateral vein

2. Palmate-net. Secondary veins originating at base of leaf with petiole main vein. Example: Maple.

hcm

FLOWERS

I. Parts

   A. Asexual

      1. Receptical—the broadened terminal portion of the flower pedicel on which the flower grows.

      2. Corolla—the flattened usually colored portion of a flower made up of the petals.

      3. Sepals—the tough usually green or brown petal-like structures growing out of the receptical just stemward of the corolla.

4. Calyx—the structure composed of all of the sepals. Acted as a protection for the flower prior to blossoming.

B. Sexual

1. Male

   a. Stamen—the entire male structure composed of both anther and filament.

   b. Anther—enlarged terminus of filament that produces the male gametophyte (pollen).

   c. Filament—long narrow structure growing out of either the receptical or the corolla that supports the anther.

2. Female

   a. Pistil—entire female organ composed of stigma, style, and ovary.

   b. Ovary—enlarged proximal portion of pistil attached to the receptical produces female gametophytes (ova), and becomes the fruit upon fertilization.

   c. Stigma—sticky distal portion of pistil that receives the pollen during pollination.

d. Style—long stem-like structure of pistil that connects the stigma and ovary. Also aids in fertilization and pollen tube formation.

II. Flower Types

A. Complete—contains all the parts of a "typical" flower (see diagram on next page).

B. Incomplete—one or more parts of a "typical" flower is missing, such as the corolla or stamens.

C. Perfect—contains both <u>male</u> and <u>female</u> parts.

D. Imperfect—either male or female parts missing.

"TYPICAL" FLOWER AND PARTS DIAGRAMATIC

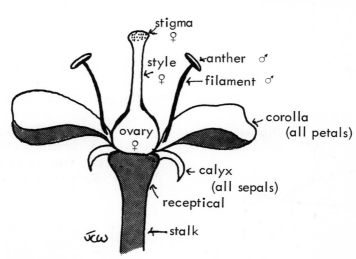

III. Ovary Location

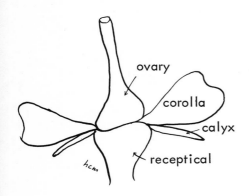

A. Superior—ovary "above" or distal to the corolla and calyx. Example: Rose.

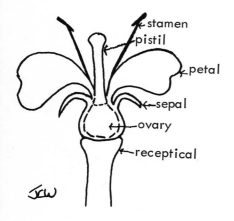

B. Inferior—ovary "below" or proximal to the corolla and calyx. Example: Fuschia.

IV. Growths

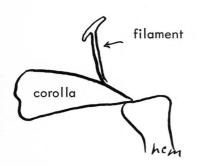

A. Agnated—two different types of structures grown together; e.g., filaments to corolla. Example: Fuschia.

B. Coalesced—two identical structures grown together; e.g.,
   filaments all united to form a
   filament tube. Example: Mal-
   low.

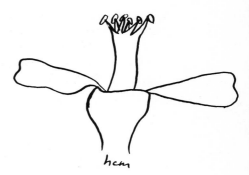

V. Arrangements

   A. Simple—one flower per recep-
      tical.

      1. Raceme—many simple flow-
         ers growing on the same
         stalk in a leaf cluster.
         Each flower attached to
         stalk by a pedicel. Ex-
         ample: Lupine.

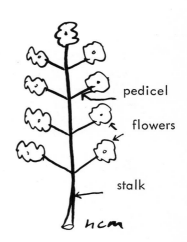

pedicel

flowers

stalk

      2. Spike—many simple flow-
         ers growing on the same
         stalk in a long cluster but
         attached directly to stalk,
         lacking pedicels. Example:
         Buckeye.

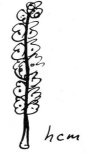

3. Umbel—many simple flowers growing from the same
stalk but on pedicels all of
which attach to terminus of
stalk. Example: Cow
Parsnips.

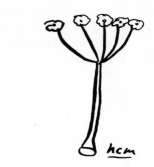

B. Composite—many flowers
growing on same receptical.
Example: Sunflower, Dan-
delion.

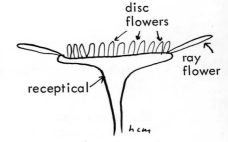

Appendix #2

A Brief Key for the Cone and Needle-leaved Trees

NEEDLES

Needles growing out of a distinct sheath
(from one place on the twig). Needles
in clusters of 1, 2, 3, 5. Large female
cones on the branches or trunks and
small male cones on the tips of the
branches.

e.g. PINES

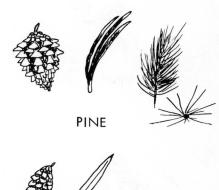

PINE

Single needles, 4-sided and borne on
short projections on the twig. The
needles are stiff and sharp and grow
from the stem in many directions.
e.g. SPRUCE

SPRUCE

Single flat, straight needles. Uniform in color on both sides (usually).
Leaf scar ovel (scar where needle
is attached to the stem).

Needles grow out in many planes.
Female cones hang down.
e.g. DOUGLAS FIR

DOUGLAS FIR

Needles grow out in 1 or 2 planes.
Small cones on the ends of the branches.
e.g. REDWOOD

REDWOOD

YEW

Medium cones on branches, not terminal.

e.g. HEMLOCK

With red berries, no cones.

e.g. YEWS

JUNIPER

SCALES OR PRICKLY NEEDLES

Scales or prickly needles wrapped around stem.

Four-sided scales with distinct light, blue, berry-like cones.

e.g. JUNIPERS

CEDAR

Flat scale-like needles with small (1 inch) indistinct round cones.

e.g. CEDARS AND CYPRESS

CYPRESS

Appendix #3

REFERENCES

Baerg, Harry J. How to Know the Western Trees. W. C. Brown and Co., 1955.

Gilliam, Howard. Weather of the San Francisco Bay Region. University of California Press, 1965.

Glen, William. Pliocene and Lower Pleistocene of the Western Part of the San Francisco Peninsula. University of California Press, 1959.

Hedgpeth, Joel W. Introduction to Seashore Life of the San Francisco Bay Region. University of California Press, 1964.

Hinds, Norman E. A. Evolution of the California Landscape. Bulletin #153, State of California Department of Natural Resources, Division of Mines, 1952.

Howard, Arthur D. Evolution of the Land Forms of the San Francisco Bay Region. University of California Press, 1965.

Ingles, Lloyd G. Mammals of the Pacific States. Stanford University Press, 1965.

Light, S. F. et al. Intertidal Invertebrates of the Central California Coast. University of California Press, 1954.

Metcalf, Woodbridge. Trees of the San Francisco Bay Region. University of California Press, 1959.

Munz, Philip A. California Spring Wildflowers. University of California Press, 1961.

Needham, J. G. and P. R. Needham. A Guide to the Study of Fresh-water Biology. Holden-Day, Inc., 1962.

Orr, Robert T. and D. B. Orr. Mushrooms. University of California Press, 1962.

Parsons, Mary E. *The Wildflowers of California.* California Academy of Sciences, 1960.

Peterson, Roger T. *A Field Guide to Western Birds.* Houghton Mifflin Co., 1961.

Pough, Richard H. *Audubon Water Birds Guide.* Doubleday and Co., 1951.

Ricketts, Edward F. and Jack Calvin. *Between Pacific Tides.* Revised by Joel W. Hedgpeth, Stanford University Press, 1968.

Robbins, C. S., Bruun, B. and Zim, S. *A Guide to Field Identification: Birds of North America.* Golden Press, New York, 1966.

Robbins, W. W., Bellue, M. K., and Ball, W. S. *Weeds of California.* State of California Printing Division, 1951.

Sharsmith, Helen K. *Spring Wildflowers of the San Francisco Bay Region.* University of California Press, 1965.

Smith, Gilbert M. *Marine Algae of the Monterey Peninsula California.* Stanford University Press, 1944.

Stebbins, Robert C. *Reptiles and Amphibians of the San Francisco Bay Region.* University of California Press, 1960.

Thomas, John H. *Flora of the Santa Cruz Mountains of California.* Stanford University Press, 1961.

Zumberge, James H. *Elements of Geology.* John Wiley & Sons, 1958.

Index

*Underscored numbers refer to illustrations

Trillium ovatum, 224
Troglodytes aedon, 195
Turdus migratorius, 193
Typha latifolia, 178
Tyrannus verticalis, 149
    T. vociferans, 149

Ulva sp. , 59
Umbellularia californica, 109, 137, 173
Urocyon cineroargenteus, 112, 157
Urolophus halleri, 26
Utrica holosericea, 176
Vaccinium ovatum, 219
    V. parvifolium, 219
Viola glabella, 225
    V. sempervirens, 225
Violet
    Redwood, 225
    Stream, 225
Vireo huttoni, 195
Vireo
    Hutton's, 195
    Yellow-throated, 196
Vitis californica, 175
Vulture
    Turkey, 117, 146

Wake Robin, 224
Warbler
    Pileolated, 194, 195
Water Boatman, 180
Water bugs, 180
Water striders, 79
Wave action, 37, 38
Waxwing, Cedar, 192
Weasel
    Long-tailed, 233
Weather, xiii-xv
Whale
    California Grey, 89, 90
    Finback, 90
    Killer, 90
Whirligig Beetles, 180
Wigglers, 66

Willet, 10
Willows
    Arroyo, 171
Wilsonia pusilla, 194
Wood Duck, 190
Woodlands, Oak
        Foothill Oak, 169, 197, 198
        Northern Oak, 169, 197, 198
        Southern Oak, 169, 197, 198
    Raparian, 169, 170
Woodpeckers
    Acorn, 137
    Downy, 247, 248
    Hairy, 248
    Redhead, 137
Woodwardia fimbriata, 222
Worms
    Circle Serpulids, 66
    Clam, 75
    Commensal, 76, 84
    Hairy-gilled, 65
    Mussel, 75
    Peanut, 78, 79
    Tube, 75
Wren
    Bewick's, 195
    House, 195, 196
    Marsh, 6
    Wrentit, 121

Xererpes fucorum, 66

Yarrow, 142
Yews, 218
Yucca sp. , 109

Zalophus californianus, 91
Zone I, 53, 56
Zone II, 58
Zone III, 70
Zone IV, 79
Zonotricha atricapilla, 119
    Z. leucophrys, 119
Zostera marina, 67